First Steps

A Guide to Setting up and Running a Successful Podiatry Practice

Tim Flanagan
Bsc (Hon) Pod MChS SRCh

Matador
9 De Montfort Mews
Leicester LE1 7FW, UK
Tel: (+44) 116 255 9311 / 9312
Email: books@troubador.co.uk
Web: www.troubador.co.uk/matador

ISBN 10: 1 905886 45 4
ISBN 13: 978-1-905886-45-6

Typeset in 11pt Stempel Garamond by Troubador Publishing Ltd, Leicester, UK
Printed in the UK by The Cromwell Press Ltd, Trowbridge, Wilts, UK

Matador is an imprint of Troubador Publishing Ltd

Dedicated to Maria, for her continual love and support.

CONTENTS

Foreword

This guide has been written to try and help you develop a successful Podiatry Practice, avoiding the pitfalls and using your money effectively.

There are skills you will need to acquire which are not always included in your Podiatry training, and are often unique to business management.

The prices quoted throughout the guide are only to demonstrate the costing of equipment and supplies, which can vary between each individual supplier. They are all excluding VAT and delivery charges and of course, change year on year. Contact the suppliers to obtain up to date catalogues, to give yourself more accurate calculations.

By following this guide, you should be able to establish a successful full time practice within two to three years. Unfortunately, things do vary slightly for everyone and so you must be prepared to be adaptable and flexible enough to overcome anything unexpected.

This book is entirely based on my own personal experience of setting up and running two practices for over 7 years and I learnt a lot of things by trial and error which have been costly. In reading this book you have taken the first steps in making the transition from being an employee to being self employed.

Tim Flanagan
August 2006

A

Starting up in Private Practice

1 Who is suited to Private Practice?

Why should anyone want to set up a Podiatry practice and work for themselves?

There are going to be many different answers to that question depending on your goals in life. Yes, a lot of people will go into private practice because they believe you can make a lot of money, which, if you are successful, you can. But at times, it can be at a more personal cost. And don't forget you can also lose a lot of money if you are unsuccessful.

'Going it alone' is a gamble, but there are certain things that can put the odds   26 in your favour – Preparation, Understanding and Realisation.

* Prepare before you start: don't jump in blindfolded or 'on a whim.'
* Understand what it is you are starting and how it will affect you and your family.
* Realise the negative side of running a business, as well as the positive. Be realistic.

Sometimes, wealth is not the only reason why people start their own business. The thought of setting up and running a successful business is personally very challenging and exciting. It can show you an additional side to Podiatry, which you may not get just from treating patients. You can also take satisfaction from the fact that if patients are returning to you time and time again, it's because they want to, not because they have to. In private practice, patients have a choice. If they don't like what you do, then they will go elsewhere and your business won't develop.

Working for yourself also gives you more freedom in your work. You work the way you want to, whether it is spending more time on certain patients or wanting a specific product for another. You organise the way the diary and clinic run to suit you best. This freedom can reduce your stress levels at work. But beware; you can only afford to be this flexible if your business is established and well organised. Although the stress levels created from time constraints may be better, you will still have the additional stress made from running the business.

Some people decide to go into private practice, solely to work on their own. If you find it difficult working in a team, or do not fit in with other colleagues at work, then private practice is definitely not for you. If you can not communicate with colleagues, there's no reason why private patients should take to you either. Your social and communication skills are essential for a successful business.

Private practitioners need to possess some or all of the following characteristics in order to succeed, as the reality of private practice will test them to the extreme.

Independence

You are on your own.

Working for yourself can be quite isolating, unless you share premises with other professionals. There will be no one to chat to at lunch times or discuss Podiatry matters with. Yes, there are patients, but for half an hour every couple of months, you cannot form strong relationships compared to those with a colleague you might see every day.

Because you are working for yourself, you have ultimate control of your destiny. You are answerable to yourself and will need to trust in the decisions you make.

Confidence

Are you strong enough and confident enough in your own abilities to build a successful business? What would happen if something came through the door you'd never seen before? You have no other colleagues to ask. Are you confident enough to cope?

Resourcefulness

Your income depends on you and you alone. You will need to learn and adapt to each of your patients needs. If you try unsuccessfully to expand the business, or waste money on unsatisfactory products, you must be resourceful enough and objective enough to learn from the experience.

Innovative

Think laterally about the needs of your patients. Provide them with what they need, in order to expand and promote your business in a more effective and profitable way.

You will also need to be innovative in relation to your competition. What sets you apart from others? What can you provide that your rivals can't or don't? Your business needs to be innovative and forward thinking; otherwise you're just the same as anyone else, so why should patients come to you instead of the Podiatrist down the road who's been established for years?

Personable

If you are not approachable or your communication skills are poor, patients will not return, even if your "hands on" Podiatry skills are excellent. Patients are paying for your time, effectively they are paying your mortgage; be nice to them. You have to be pleasant to them even if you personally feel unhappy. It's not about pampering to their every whim, it's about being professional and having good personal relations (PR) skills.

Your communication skills can make or break a successful business. You will also need to develop your skills at recognising non verbal cues and responding to them in order to 'read' your patients temperament or mood for that day. If you get it wrong, you could say or do something inappropriate and they might not return.

Dedication

Because you are in charge and the running of the business is dependent on you, you cannot just take a day off sick if you don't feel up to a day's work because of a late night out. You have got to be dedicated to the business and that means making the extra effort to go into work.

Unfortunately, you may also have to work outside normal working hours, but for the business to be successful and grow, you have to have this level of dedication. You will have to do paperwork and general running of the business at home and not just the hands on practical side of Podiatry. This can affect your home and social life and you will need to rely on the support, patience and understanding of your partner, friends and family.

The bottom line is: if you don't work, you don't get paid and your business is not making money. Your home or other assets you have will then be at risk if your business fails with debts.

You will also need a certain dedication to your patients. Doing something more than just treating them for the half hour they are in your clinic. For example, finding out for them the phone number of the company who makes the shoes you were discussing during the treatment. This helps the patient, but it also helps the business when the patient tells their friends how helpful you were and they book an appointment too.

You have got to be prepared and dedicated enough to put in the extra effort and commitment to the business and patients, your income depends on it.

Responsibility

You are responsible for everything you do in private practice. If you do something wrong, it's your fault. There is no one else to blame. No one else can make new patients come, or keep existing patients returning or make the business succeed but you.

You are the business, without you, it won't work.

Competency

If you are not good at your job, your business will fail. Bad patient reports travel a lot faster than good feedback. You will have to be prepared to invest personally in yourself and your skills in order to maintain and develop them through regular professional and business training courses. Every treatment you provide is being judged by each patient.

Some of these characteristics should already be part of your professional make up, but to succeed in private practice your survival is dependent on them.

If you prefer the safety and security of working in paid employment, where you have the knowledge that you will bring home a wage every month, then private practice is probably not the area of podiatry to which you would be most suited.

If, however, after reading the above, you are still excited by the challenge of setting up and running a private practice, then read on. The journey will not always be easy, but it is financially, personally and professionally rewarding.

2 Planning a Business

As a business your prime objective is to sell things over and over again for more money than it costs to do so. What you are selling is your service and treatment. The business will need to make a profit in order to survive, prosper and expand. It also needs to weather fluctuations in the market. It may be that several years after you have established a practice, a rival practice is set up in your area which offers a service at a lower price. This will affect your business. Would your business survive a decline in profit, or have sufficient funds to adapt and compete with the rival? Detailed planning at the start of the business and constant referral back to a business plan will help keep the business moving forward positively.

A business plan is a worthwhile exercise. If you are relying on funding to get the business off the ground, your investors will require a thorough business plan, with a cash flow forecast. If you are self funding, you should still complete a business plan to give yourself a clearer understanding of set up costs, running costs, costs of promotion and of your competitors. If you are investing your own money and time into a project, it has got to be worthwhile and have the potential to succeed.

The information you will require to complete a comprehensive Business Plan is looked at in greater detail in other chapters within this section. Refer to them as you go through and complete this plan.

A business plan is divided into a number of sections:

1. Business Details
2. Objectives and Aims
3. Staff (including yourself)
4. Premises
5. Equipment
6. Services Available

7.   Customers

8.   Competitors

9.   Promotion

10.   Funding

11.   Personal Survival Budget

12.   Pricing

13.   Financial Projections

14.   Personal Asset Statement

15.   Cash flow Forecast

A skeleton business plan is included in Appendix A for your completion

I.   Business Details

What are you going to call your business? Will it be in your name or have you decided to make up a name for the clinic? Keep it professional. A name is important as part of your first impression to potential customers. If you decide to call your business or clinic with a name, make sure is conveys the right message.

Don't forget to include the clinic address, phone numbers and e-mail and website addresses if you have one on your business plan.

You will also need to decide on which Legal status will be right for your business. There are several structures to choose from, all of which have different implications on certain aspects of the business including;

* Tax and National Insurance
* Accounts
* Your financial liability
* Management of the business

Most Private Practices will start as Sole Traders or as a Partnership.

A Sole Trader is the most straightforward of all the legal statuses. You are personally responsible for all the debts the business accumulates, therefore if your business fails, your home and other assets which you have, will be at risk. All profits that the business makes however, are yours. All the decisions for running the business are made by you. You will need to submit an annual self assessment tax return to HM Revenue and Customs as well as keep income and expenses accounts relating to the business. Profits that the business makes are taxed and you will need to pay fixed rate Class 2 National Insurance contributions and Class 4 National Insurance Contributions. (See the chapter on Accounting and Book Keeping for more details.)

Another status of trading is as a Partnership. Instead of working on your own, you go into the business with one or more people, who share the risks, debts, decision making and profits. The big advantage of a Partnership is that each partner will be bringing to the business a different set of expertise. An agreement between partners will need to be written and signed by all parties. It is best to do this through a solicitor to make a legally binding contract between you all. If a partner dies or leaves, the partnership will need to dissolve, although this will not require the business to stop trading, merely a new Partnership agreement drawn up. 'Sleeping' partners are those that help to raise finance to help start or build the business, but take no particular part in the running and management of the business. The business, as well as each individual partner will need to submit self assessment tax returns to HM Revenue and Customs. Each partner is taxed on their share of the profits.

If you are unsure of which form your business should take then consult a Solicitor or Accountant for their advice.

Because you will be classed as self-employed you will also need to register with HM Revenue and Customs and can do this by downloading the appropriate forms from their website. Contact details for this are included in Appendix B. You can still work as an employee, for example in the NHS, at the same time as being self employed, but you must still register.

In this section, also include a brief outline of what you will be doing or selling in the business. Don't forget non Podiatrists will be reading your business plan, i.e. investors, so keep it clear and simple to understand.

2.   Objectives and Aims

Break up your objectives into three time spans. They should reflect realistic goals, achievable over one, two and three or five years. These are called your short, medium and long term objectives.

Example

Short Term Objectives
Start trading and 'break even' (achieve neither a loss nor profit) by the end of the first year.

Medium Term Objectives
To be trading at a profit by the end of the second year
Pay off equipment and investors

Long Term Objectives
Running at a profit with reduced advertising costs within five years
Have no debts to investors
Have clinic running at near to capacity

Your objectives need to be realistic and achievable. They will also be personal to you, depending on where you want to take the business and what your future aims are. Do you want to employ people in the future? If you solely own or lease the premises, will you be letting rooms out to other professionals?

We all have specific ideas of what we want out of private practice and how far we want to expand it. Write you ultimate aim for the business and when you think you could achieve it.

3.   Staff

Although you may not intend to employ staff when you start, you will still need to include yourself in this section. You are the most important member of staff.

As well as your name, date of birth and role within the business you should also include your qualifications, experience and other relevant jobs you have had. What training have you received in addition to your professional qualifications?

What staff might you need to employ? If you join a practice which has a shared reception you will not need to pay the receptionist's wages, tax or national insurance directly, that will be the responsibility of the person you are paying the rent to.

If you will be employing staff, include their role within the business and what experience they can bring. Include a complete CV for yourself and key members of staff as an addition at the back of your business plan.

4. Premises

In this section include information about the premises you intend to work from. If it is freehold (you are buying it and paying a mortgage) include its value, as well as mortgage information. If renting, what will the monthly rent be and who is it payable to? What are the annual lease-hold costs and how long is the contract for? If you are freehold or lease-hold you will also be responsible for payment of business rates. This is payable to your local county council. To find out how much it is likely to be, you can contact the council and they should be able to give you a rough idea. Include this cost in your business plan together with its annual renewal date. If you are renting a room, business rates should be included for you.

If freehold or leasehold, the insurance for the practice is also your responsibility and you will need public liability, contents and buildings insurance. Some insurance companies link all of these together so you only need to pay one premium a month for all. If renting a room, you may still require insurance for your equipment which is left in the practice. In the business plan include your premiums for insurance as well as a brief explanation of what is covered and how much it is covered for. When is the annual renewal date?

This might only be the start of the business, but you need to think whether the premises will be adequate for your future requirements. It needs to have potential for growth.

5. Equipment

List the equipment you require and the approximate costs, as well as how long you would estimate the equipment to last? The length equipment will last is pure guesswork, but talk to other Podiatrists or Professionals who use similar equipment and ask how long theirs lasted. How long are the guarantees on new equipment? How will you cope with unexpected expenses or repairs of second hand equipment?

Is it worth buying second hand? Look in your journals for people selling second hand equipment. Although it may be cheaper you may also have to budget for maintenance and spare parts early on in the business.

6.   Service Available

Who is your business aimed at? If it's mainly routine Podiatry it's likely to be middle aged to elderly people, with some disposable income to enable them to afford private Podiatry. If you aim to provide a mainly biomechanics service, your business may be aimed more at a younger, sportier market. Make a list of what services you will provide and try and estimate what percentage each service will contribute to your business.

Depending on the services you provide and how your clinic is set up will decide the percentage of time you share between each service.

If you start the clinic with routine Podiatry, what services do you intend to develop and introduce to the practice in the future? Will this involve additional training and the introduction of more equipment?

You also need to consider the amount of disposable stock you will need. It is difficult to estimate this until you start, but try to work out what the maximum amount of stock you will need for one treatment. Then estimate the cost for the first one hundred treatments. As the number of patients increases over time so will the amount of stock you will require. Look at the supplier's terms of payment. Some allow you up to 30 days to pay, so you can provide treatments and collect money before actually paying for the goods. This helps with your cash flow.

Example

Complete Service	
Routine	60%
Biomechanics	10%
Diabetic reviews	10%
Nail Surgery	5%
Domicilaries	15%

Biomechanics Clinic	
Biomechanics	85%
Routine	15%

Domiciliary Only	
Routine	95%
Biomechanics	5%

7. Customers

Who are your potential customers? Think about why patients would want to come to you rather that your competitors. Look at the population of the town or city you intend to work in and what proportion are potential patients. What percentage are elderly people with a disposable income? Is the area affluent or deprived? Do some research at your local library or on the Internet to have a better understanding of your intended area. Visit the website *http://neighbourhood.statistics.gov.uk/dissemination/* for comprehensive information on population, health, age etc.

8. Competitors

Who will be your main competitors and what are their strengths and weaknesses? What do they charge? Consider the length of time they have been working there and listen to opinions people have of them. Essentially, they are going to provide a similar service, so you have to make the patients want to come to you time and time again. How will you do this? It could be achieved by providing a professional, modern and clean clinic, with a developing reputation for thorough, effective and comprehensive treatment. If you can maintain high professional standards and good communication skills, your reputation will keep patients coming back to you.

9. Promotion

How do you intend to promote yourself and attract new patients to you? Read the chapter on marketing and advertising to give you ideas and advice on where best to spend your money. Write in your business plan where you intend to spend your advertising budget and how much it might approximately cost. Realistically, how much business do you think it will bring in? Look at circulation numbers of publications you advertise in, and include that in the business plan.

How many patients do you plan to treat within the first 6 months and then the following 6 months? Don't forget that people die, move away or have their problems cured, so you will need to regularly promote and advertise the practice to keep a continual stream of new patients coming into the clinic to replace those lost. As time goes on, you will be able to spend less on advertising as word of mouth and recommendation increases.

10. Funding

Work out how much capital (the money you will need to introduce into the business) you are going to require to start the business and manage it for the first few months. Write down the start up costs, which should include your equipment, stock, rent, lease or mortgage repayment for the first three months, advertising, stationary, telephone and insurance or anything else you think you will need at the beginning.

You are also going to need to live on something for the first three months, so include your monthly personal expenses in this. You can work your personal expenses out in the survival budget later in your business plan.

The capital is the amount of money you are going to need to inject into the business to get it off the ground. How much of it are you personally going to stake in the business? Most investors will want to see you have put your own money at risk, in order to encourage them to put theirs in as well.

In preparation for your business, go to your local business enterprise agency or business link, who will be able to give you free advice, as well as up to date information on grants or loans. See also the chapter on Funding for advice on the different forms of investment you can acquire.

11. Personal Survival Budget

In order to have an idea of what amount of money you personally are going to need to survive on, you will need to work out what your survival budget is. This will also help you to calculate the pricing of the services you intend to provide in the clinic.

If you are coming into a new business from employment, you are probably going to have to adjust your lifestyle a little to start with, to reduce the impact of the business on your life. You are not going to have so much free cash available to you for the first year, so think about working part time whilst you build up your private practice, to provide you with some guaranteed household income.

A personal survival budget is based on your household expenses, not the expenses created from the business. This is about you, your family and your house. List all your expenses including your mortgage or rent, utility bills and any hire purchases you have. A list is included in Appendix A. From your total yearly expenditure, subtract any household income, from your partner or any other sources. The figure you are left with is your survival income, i.e. this is the amount of drawings (wages) you will need to take from the business in the first year in order to cover all your household expenses and maintain the lifestyle you require.

Example

Bob Supermax intends leaving full time employment and has decided to set up as a private Podiatrist.

He lives with his wife, who brings in a yearly salary of £12,000, in a two bedroom house and is paying a mortgage of £600 a month. Bob has decided to keep a part time job for 2 days a week for the first year, to keep some income coming into the house whilst the practice grows. This will bring in another £5,000.

The following is Bob's Personal Survival Budget for a year, i.e. this is the amount of money the business must provide. He will require at least £5,990 from his new business in the first year in order for him to continue to meet repayments for all his household expenses.

His household expenses are broken down as follows;

Expenditure	Yearly cost
Mortgage Repayment	£7,200
Savings	£2,400
Car Repayments	£3,000
HP Repayments	£2,000
Food	£2,300
Petrol	£1,800
Council Tax	£1,200
Socialising	£1,400
Utilities	£800
Life Insurance	£300
Telephone	£300
Insurance	£240
Subscriptions	£50
Total Expenditure	£22,990
Household Income	£17,000
Personal Survival Budget	**£5,990**

12. Pricing

Your pricing is crucial to make your business successful. If you pitch it too high, patients won't come, too low and you won't cover your expenses and will have to work harder to make a profit. Look at what other Podiatrists are charging and pitch yourself against that. Try to aim at the middle to lower end to start with, to make yourself competitive. You can always put your prices up at a later stage, when you are more established.

To work out your pricing you have to base it on what your business expenses are, together with how much you will need to take out of the business to cover your Personal Survival Budget. Show how you have worked out your prices and how they compare with your competitors in your business plan.

Example

Bob is now trying to work out how much he should charge for a routine Podiatry treatment which will last 30 mins. Based on his calculations below, and after researching his competitor's prices, he has decided to charge £17 for routine treatment. This will leave him £6.14 profit from each patient which will help to cover other costs acquired through vacant appointments, advertising or any unexpected expenses such as maintenance or repair.

As Bob increases the hours that he works it will also increase the amount of profit he makes per treatment (see the table opposite).

Explanation of the table opposite
It is very difficult to calculate what material you will use and how much it will cost. By breaking down packs and boxes into singular units you can estimate what the cost would be in treating one patient. The rent is based on working an eight hour day costing £50, so divide it into cost per hour then cost per half hour treatment. Wear and tear on equipment is an estimate. 25,000 treatments is approximately a life span of about 6–7 years in a full time practice. Your Personal Survival Budget for the year will need to be divided into a week, then the number of hours worked in that week, then per half hour treatment. You will be taxed on the price you charge the patients, so budget for tax and National Insurance Contributions.

Expenditure	Basis of calculation	Cost	Formulae
Possible Materials Used		£ 1 . 00	
Rent	Based on an 8 hour day costing £50 rent	£ 3 . 13	£50 / 8 / 2
Use of equipment	Based on life span of 25,000 treatments, costing £4,000	£ 0 . 16	£4,000 / 25,000
Personal Survival Budget	£5,990 per year, working a 24 hour week	£ 2 . 40	£5990 / 52 / 24 / 2
	Sub Total	£ 6 . 69	
Savings for Tax	17.5%	£ 2 . 98	£17 X 0.175
Savings for National Insurance	7%	£ 1 . 19	£17 X 0.07
	Total	£ 10 . 86	
	Profit per treatment	£ 6 . 14	£17 - £10.86

13. Financial Projections

Because you are just starting a business, a financial projection is quite a hard thing to work out. What you are going to provide is pure guess work, but with thorough research you can make a projection based on educated guess work.

To start with, work out what your gross profit for the year could be. Basically, this is the total amount of money your business could take before any expenses are taken off. From these figures you will also be able to work out your gross profit margin.

Example

Bob is going to charge £17 for every routine treatment he provides. He is aiming to provide 35 routine treatments in the first month, rising by 6 each month, so the total number of treatments for the year would be

816 at £17, therefore Bob's projected sales would be £13,872.

The direct costs of providing this, are the costs of your stock and supplies. Subtracting this from the projected sales will give Bob his gross profit. If you estimate the costs at £1 per treatment his gross profit would be £13,056, i.e. £13,872 - £816.

Bob's gross profit margin is:

$$(£13,056 / 13,872) \times 100 = \textbf{94.12\%}$$
$$(\text{Gross Profit} / \text{Projected Sales}) \times 100 = \text{Gross Profit Margin}$$

You will now need to catalogue all the expenses you expect to incur over your first year.

Example

Bob needs to take £5,990 as his drawings from the business in the first year. Because Bob doesn't have many patients to start with he only works one day a week in the practice for the first 3 months, expanding to 2 days a week for the following 9 months to keep his costs down. His rent on the premises for the year would be £4,200. This includes all his utilities and rates. He is going to have a mobile phone to run his business, on a monthly contract of £20. His yearly phone costs would therefore be £240. In order to attain new patients Bob has decided to invest £100 per month for the first year, the total being £1,200. Initially he borrowed £4,000 to purchase the equipment, which he intends to pay off over 2 years. The first years repayments plus interest totals £2,250. Bob's total overheads are £13,880.

Expenses	Cost
Drawings	£5,990
Rent	£4,200
Telephone	£240
Advertising	£1,200
HP Repayments	£2,250
Total	**£13,880**

Using these figures you can now calculate what your annual turnover is in order to break even, which you can then use to estimate what your monthly turnover will need to be.

Example

Bob's annual turnover to break even is:

$$(£13,880 / 94.12\%) \times 100 = \textbf{£14,747}$$

(Overheads / Gross Profit Margin) × 100 = Break Even Turnover

By subtracting the break even turnover from the projected sales, Bob can work out his profit, if any. If Bob's financial projection is accurate then in the first year he will make a small loss of £875. In order to survive the first year whilst his business becomes established, he may have to reduce some of his personal spending at home. During the first year, a business is lucky to break even. As the business grows and develops, your overheads may increase, but so will your gross profit.

I know all these figures may seem a bit daunting, but follow the formulae in Appendix A, and you should be able to give yourself a rough guide on what you should be aiming for each month.

14. Personal Asset Statement

If an investor is lending you money to help start the business, they are going to want to know that their money is safe. In order to do this, you must provide them with a Personal Asset Statement. This is a list of all your assets and what other liabilities you already have. If the business fails, investors will want to be sure that they will still get their money back from sources other than a failed business. This seems pretty heartless, but investors don't want to throw their money away. This is why you have to be serious and confident about your business, because if it fails you could lose more than just your pride. Your home could be at risk, if you cannot meet the payments owing to the investors.

Start by listing your Assets, the biggest of which is your home, if you own it. Any savings you have, insurance policies, investments or shares should also be listed as well as other items you own, i.e. your vehicle. You then need to work out your liabilities. What is your current mortgage outstanding? What repayments do you still have on HP or loans? Subtract your liabilities from your assets to work out your Personal Net Asset.

15. Cash flow forecast

The movement of money, from spending it to earning it is called Cash Flow.

A cash flow forecast is useful in providing you with an idea of when certain bills will need paying, so you can budget and prepare the business for payments. For your business to succeed, you will need to have cash flowing through your business, in order to maintain and develop it. Predicting certain payments is difficult, but there will be certain payments which may be required on certain dates or at certain intervals. Think carefully about your cash flow for the next 12 months, and as the first 6 months pass compare the actual cash flow with your predicted budget cash flow. Half way through the first 6 months, redo the latter 6 months of the year as you will have a better understanding of what you are expecting your cash flow to be. A lot of the work you have already done in this business plan and the figures you have come up with, will help you complete your cash flow forecast.

Presenting a Business Plan

Now that you have completed a comprehensive business plan, chances are you will need to present it to someone else. It may be a bank or investor who is going to put money into the business at the beginning, or maybe a committee to attain an award or grant for developing the business. Whatever the reason is, you need to make sure that your plan and presentation has the desired effect.

* Keep the plan clear and concise. It is less likely to be read if there is a lot of text and information. Put key information down as bullet points for the reader to scan.

* Make sure the plan is professional, it is conveying an image about the potential business and how it will be conducted.

* Include a contents page at the beginning and number each page and section.

* Print your plan rather than writing it by hand — it's clearer, more legible and much more professional.

* Include a Summary at the beginning containing the key points, including financial projections, opportunities and featured highlights of the plan. The aim of a good summary is to entice the investor to want to read the plan in more detail because the idea and prospects appeal to them. Make your summary a maximum of two pages long, concise but interesting.

* Get your plan bound so that pages do not get lost or mixed up.

* If you are emailing your plan, it will need to be in a format which is universally read on other computers, such as Microsoft Word.

* Before you present the plan to anyone, get at least two friends or family members to read it. They may be able to point out grammar or spelling mistakes you overlooked as well as suggesting areas that may need rewriting to improve clarity.

* Avoid including a list of data in the main plan. Include them in Appendices at the back.

* Overall, make sure the plan is realistic. If it is not, potential investors will doubt your abilities to manage a business if they feel that your goals and financial predictions are unattainable.

Once you have completed your business plan, keep it safe and refer back to it at regular intervals. It is a comprehensive guide to your business and can help improve and develop the business in the future.

3 Seeking Advice and Expertise

Setting up a business can be quite complicated and along the way you will come across many things which you might not understand or be aware of. There are many ways of getting help and advice, some of which you will have to pay for but many others which are free.

Accountant

An Accountant can give you guidance and advice on the financial aspect of your business. Employing the use of an Accountant is well worth it. Their fees may seem to be high, but they are going to save you a lot of hard work and prevent you from scratching your head over figures which don't add up the day before your tax return is due.

There are many different types of Accountants available to use. A Chartered or Certified Accountant should suit your needs as a small business.

Accountants are qualified professionals who have a greater understanding of the latest tax and business changes than you and I, so don't struggle trying to do them yourself. Accountants also know about what expenses are allowed in your business and which can be deducted against your tax. This can save you a lot of money, as you will not be paying Tax which needn't be paid.

Bank Services

Setting up a business bank account is a useful part of starting a business. As well as being able to manage your money they can provide you with valuable free advice on all aspects of business. It is in their interest to help you make your business succeed.

Look around at what is available from different banks. In recent years they have become a lot more flexible and will try to attract you with offers or promotions. But don't be persuaded by glamorous gifts or promises. Look at the bare bones of their services; you should be able to get a service which includes all or some of the following:

* Free business advice

* Low monthly charges (In some cases this might actually be free for the first 12 or 24 months)

* Low charges for paying into and out of your account (In some cases this might actually be free for the first 12 or 24 months)

* Interest paid to your account when you are in credit

* Free Telephone and Internet banking

* A designated Business banker

* Business tools and information designed to help you develop your practice

* Low rate credit card (In some cases there may be no annual fee for the first 12 months)

You will be charged for transactions on your account every month, but fees vary between banks, so shop around. Transactions include paying money into the account, issuing a cheque or paying a standing order or direct debit. A monthly running charge is also applied to your account on behalf of your bank in payment for managing and running your account.

A normal current bank account would not allow you to put in the volume of cheques that a business would generate, nor would it provide you with the free advice relating to your business.

If there are aspects of the business which you need information about, your designated business manager should beable to point you in the right direction or provide you with the answers you need.

Business Link

This is a service funded by the Department of Trade and Industry as well as other government departments and local authorities as part of the government's campaign to help promote and develop small businesses. They provide free information, advice and support on all aspects of your business and can be accessed online, on the telephone or in local advice offices. To find your nearest one call 0845 600 9006.

Although Business Link is an English based advice service, the rest of the UK has equivalent services, of which, contact details can be found in Appendix B.

Business Eye	Wales
Invest Northern Ireland	Northern Island
Business Gateway	Glasgow
Highlands and Islands Enterprise	Scotland

HM Revenue and Customs

Contact the Inland Revenue for free advice on tax and finances. They also have the relevant forms on their web site for you to download to make registering easier and quicker.

National Federation of Enterprise Agencies (NFEA)

This is a network of independent agencies that provide a comprehensive range of services for small businesses. The NFEA help to support new businesses and encourage growth and stability. To find your nearest NFEA member, visit the web site listed in Appendix B. The NFEA is involved with the Business Volunteer Mentor Programme, which provides free mentoring from volunteers to people starting a new business or already running a small business. They also run the Small Business Advice Service, providing free internet based advice for entre- preneurs and the self employed, from professional business advisers.

Federation of Small Businesses (FSB)

The FSB was formed in 1974 and, for a small fee, promotes and protects the interests of the self employed and small business owners. It operates a 24 hour legal helpline, as well as giving advice on finance, government policies, business banking, Insurance and vehicle solutions. Other services include sample contracts of employment, business magazine and newsletter pertaining to local issues.

Shell LiveWIRE

As part of their contribution to small businesses and enterprise, the oil company Shell provides free information and support to 16-30 year olds who are starting up their own business. They have a network of local business advisers and young business mentors as well as an interactive web service and idea exchange. Businesses also have the chance to win financial awards through LiveWIRE.

Membership to LiveWIRE includes:

* Interactive learning sections to help people develop business ideas.

* Core business learning modules.

* Opportunity to win over £10,000 and the title Shell LiveWIRE Young Entrepreneur of the year.

* Discussion forum to share experiences and advice.

* Mentor system.

* Finance Action Planner to help develop financial skills and produce financial forecasts and reports.

Solicitor

For a fee, a Solicitor will advise you on legal issues regarding your business, as well as draw up legal documents for rental agreements, contracts of employment, Partnership agreements etc. Overall, most general legal advice applicable to a small business can be found free of charge through business support groups such as others in this section.

4 Finding Premises

No matter how good you are at running a business or how competent a clinician you are, if your clinic is in the wrong location, patients will not come. It's no good setting up a clinic in a town already served by half a dozen established Podiatrists or on the top floor of a building, where the access for patients who are likely to have mobility difficulties would be awkward.

Your premises need to be flexible and meet your current and future requirements. If they don't meet your future needs then you don't want to be tied into long rental contracts, restricting you from moving.

What will your future requirements be? Is the room available for you to use every day of the week once you have become established? Does the lease run out in a couple of years? Will the location be less desirable as a clinic if there are developments planned around it?

Requirements for a location

Most of your patients will be elderly, so you have to think of their particular needs. Make a list of what you think their needs are, as well as your own and stick to it, don't be put off your list by rent which may be cheaper but no where near your patients.

The location of the clinic in relation to shops, bus routes, doctors and hairdressers is important to older people as they often like to get several things done in one trip. For example, if they have an appointment at the hairdressers, they may like to combine it with their Podiatry appointment or a shopping trip. Therefore, having a practice too far away from other amenities is not a good idea.

How much competition do you want? If there are too many Podiatrists already in the area then one more wouldn't be necessary. If there are no existing practices in the area, find out why not. Maybe the population is such that there is not much call for a Podiatrist? Perhaps there are other alternative provisions for residents. When no business already exists, it is not always a great opportunity, so do thorough research before embarking on your business in that location.

Elderly people also have mobility problems, so make it easier for them to get to you. Be conveniently near a bus stop along a main route and don't be too far up or down a flight of stairs. If your patients do have to ascend stairs make sure there are handrails, or better sill purpose built disabled access.

Since October 2004, the Disability Discrimination Act (1995) has required businesses to take steps to address physical barriers to disabled people who want to access their services or premises. There should be a reasonable means of entering the building, so a ramp may be required instead of steps, or larger signs for those with visual diabilities. There are some grants available locally for business to adjust their premises to aid disabled visitors. Check with your local council to see what is available for you.

Desirable Clinic Requirements

➢   Near local amenities
➢   Near a Bus Stop along a main route
➢   Near a parking area
➢   On the ground floor
➢   With other therapists or professionals in the same building or nearby
➢   In an area with a high proportion of elderly people
➢   In an area with minimal Podiatry services
➢   One with scope for future needs
➢   In a building in good repair
➢   In a building with good security and a low crime rate
➢   One which already meets health and safety standards and fire and building regulations

---

When you are deciding on your premises, look at the property itself; does it convey the right image? If you're going to rent with a shared reception, are the receptionists friendly and efficient? If not, you will lose patients before they've even met you.

Think of the size of space you will need. If you are only treating one person at a time, with perhaps one or two people waiting for their appointments, would you need a large waiting area or clinic? If you intend to do gait analysis have you the space to include a treadmill or walkway?

As well as professional requirements you should also consider statutory ones too. Consider the physical state of the building and work space. Would improvements be required to bring them up to health and safety standards, fire regulations or building regulations?

Check the security of the building. Look at crime rates on the statistics site listed in Appendix B. If the local crime figures and security of the building are poor, it will reflect in the premium of your insurance.

Choosing Premises

Get a map of the town or area you are interested in working in and look at the bus routes and locations of shops and other amenities. Outline with a red pen an area on the map which includes the majority of these facilities. This will be your prime location area. Walk this area and make a note of any practices which don't have a podiatrist working within them and that fit your criteria for a desirable clinic with possibilities to rent. Also, look to see which shops are vacant in the area which could be converted to become a suitable practice.

When you have a list of premises, write to them, introducing yourself and what you do and enquire about rooms to rent. Follow this up with a phone call a week later, or better still, go into the practice and talk to the practice manager or landlord. Ask how much the rent would be and whether you could rent the room by the day. This is cheaper for you as you only pay for the room when you use it. Ask what is included in the rent and whether there are any additional things to which you would need to contribute. How long would the rent remain at that cost? Get it fixed for a minimum of at least one year so you can budget much more easily.

Some landlords don't have fixed rents but take a percentage of your gross income, which can sometimes be as high as 50%, but should ideally be between 20-40%. This arrangement might suit you to start with as you slowly increase the amount of work you do, but for the long term a fixed rent is more suitable.

If you decided to take on a lease of a property, you will need to find out what is available. Go into all the local estate agents and enquire about commercial properties for lease, not all estate agents will deal with commercial property. The annual leasehold costs will be on the property details and some may even have the approximate costs of business rates and utilities.

The Local Enterprise Agency and Local Authority sometimes have lists of commercial property available.

When purchasing property freehold to use as a business, you will need to apply to the local council for planning permission to convert the use of the house from a home to a business, if it is not already being used as a business.

Deciding whether to rent, lease or buy is a difficult decision and is looked at in more detail in a later chapter.

Working from Home

There are many benefits in working from home, but also many disadvantages.

It is very convenient, cheap, has no travel expenses and certain financial benefits. But as part of your mortgage agreement you may not be allowed to run a business from your home. The council may also not allow you to run a business from home. Don't forget that having patients come to your home can be quite intrusive and they may contact you outside office hours or at weekends or evenings. They may even turn up while you are having your Sunday lunch wanting to book an appointment. It is often better to keep your work and home life separate. Doing paperwork at home will not intrude quite so much and will probably be necessary, but try to keep patients away from your home.

If you do decide to set up a clinic at home and you have permission from the local council, and it is not going to affect your neighbours in any way, then you will need to make sure that your home insurance is adequate. You may need to increase it to cover additional equipment as well as public liability. You will also need to have a health and safety and fire inspection to make sure it complies with certain regulations, so it may require some modifications, in order to comply.

5 Renting, Leasing or Buying Options

There are different ways to obtain premises suitable to work from; you have to decide which option is right for you and which will meet your current and future requirements.

Renting

This is the cheapest of the options, but a great way of getting the business up and running with minimal costs. If you rent you will be paying for the room you use, which should include electricity, water and other utility bills.

If you can work within an already working practice it has numerous advantages and very few disadvantages.

* Your monthly expenses are fixed until the rent is reviewed

* It has low start up costs

* The room you rent will probably be supplied at a standard ready for immediate use

* If that practice has other therapists working there (i.e. Dentists, Doctors, Physiotherapists), you will have a steady flow of potential patients already coming through the door who may book an appointment with you as well. This is good free advertising.

* If you rent a room from a landlord, you should get clerical assistance (i.e. booked telephone appointments), electricity, water and business rates included within your rent.

* If you are renting, you do not own the room or building, so the business has no asset at the end of the agreement or when you decide to move.

* There may be some restrictions imposed on you by the landlord to do with hours of work, advertising or the volume of clerical work generated.

A rental agreement will be drawn up, which may be open ended or fixed to a certain number of years. You will need to sign this agreement before you start working, but read it thoroughly and seek legal advice if you are unsure.

Leasing

This is a relatively simple and cost effective way of acquiring premises for your business. Most small businesses will not have the capital to buy premises from the beginning, so this is a good alternative, allowing your capital to be used in other areas such as purchasing equipment and advertising.

Taking a leasehold on, usually involves a whole building or one floor. You will still not own the building, but you can sub-let rooms to other therapists or professionals and generate additional income to help pay your overheads. You can also sell the business with years left on the lease, thereby generating an asset within the business.

Features of a Lease agreement include:

* You pay an agreed rent for a fixed number of years. Some agreements allow the rent to reviewed and adjusted after a specified time.

* Low start up costs.

* You will need to pay Legal fees for the agreement

* There may be a refundable deposit to pay at the start

* There may be maintenance to do before you can move in

* Because you have an agreement, they can be restricting if you need to move premises before the lease ends. You would need to sell the lease so someone else takes it on

* Stamp duty will need to be paid on a commercial Lease

* You will need to pay monthly Business rates to your local authority

As the occupier of the building, you have a shared legal responsibility with the landlord to ensure it meets Health and Safety requirements for employees as well as patients who visit the premises. Health and Safety requirements are discussed in greater detail later in the book.

There is a certain agreement called a Licence agreement which allows you to rent the premises with low start up costs. You are not responsible for any structural repairs, but you are expected to maintain the premises in good order.

Before you sign any agreement you should seek legal advice to make sure it is exactly what you want.

Buying

Although it is appealing to own the premises you intend to work from, it is a costly and risky purchase for a budding small business.

Freehold is when you effectively purchase the property and you will have a mortgage similar to the one on a house. At the end of the mortgage term you will own the building. Features of Buying include:

* You have overall control of the premises

* You have an asset which is saleable should you choose to move or retire

* The monthly costs are relatively stable as there is no one to increase rent every year

* Within Legal guidelines, you have control over the appearance and alterations which are done on the property

* The value of the property may rise

* The value of the property may fall

* Start up costs can be high, you will need to pay legal fees, stamp duty and any planning application fees

* You are responsible for anything relating to the building including all maintenance and repairs

* You must comply to Health and Safety requirements, Building regulations, Fire Regulations, Public Liability Insurance and Building Insurance etc

* You will need to pay Business Rates to you Local Authority

Because you own the building you have a lot more responsibilities to adhere to than when renting or leasing a property. You will need to apply for planning permission from the local authority to get permission to use the building as a Podiatry clinic. You will have to meet minimum workplace standards and provide a suitable working environment as well as provide access facilities for disabled patients.

To meet the required minimum standards for a suitable working environment for your staff and patients, you will need to provide;

* Adequate washing and toilet facilities for all, including the disabled

* Have a seating area for staff to eat and provide facilities for hot drinks

* Have a smoking policy and smoke free seating area

* Display safety information

* Maintain work areas which are well ventilated and spacious

* Allocate storage and changing facilities for staff.

6 Obtaining Planning Permission

Planning consent is generally required if you are building or extending a building, but you will probably not need to consider applying for these purposes. Instead, it will be more relevant to you that planning consent will be required from your local authority if you wish to change a buildings use, for example if you are leasing or buying your premises and the use of the building was different to what you now intend to use it as. It is also needed if you intend to change the external appearance of the building or put up signs or shop fascias.

If your building is in a conservation area or is listed, you will need to contact your local authority to explain what you intend to do, as tighter restrictions govern these types of buildings.

If you are unsure whether planning permission is going to be required you can submit a free informal application to the authority, but it may take up to 8 weeks to get a response. This will then advise you if a formal application will be required.

Never start work or start altering premises before you have planning permission. The local authority has the ability to serve you with an enforcement notice to change what work you have done on the building or cease trading.

If you need to apply for planning consent, you should first contact your local authority and have an informal meeting with the planning officer, explaining what your proposals are.

With a formal application, you will need to submit plans and details of your premises and what you intend to do. You will also need to pay for a formal application. Contact your authority, who will be able to inform you of the cost of an application.

Once you have applied, the local authority will contact your neighbours to advise them of your proposal, allowing them chance to voice any objections they may have. They may also put an announcement in the local newspaper. A decision on your application will be made at a monthly meeting of the council. You can attend this meeting if you wish, but it is not essential. Decisions are usually made within 8 weeks of applying.

7 Buying an Existing Business

This may seem like an appealing option. There are no immediate start up costs, except the price of purchasing the business, and maybe updating some of the equipment, but you have an already developed patient list and hopefully a well running profitable business.

Before you decide on purchasing an already established business you will need to take a lot of things into consideration. Firstly you will probably need to find a more substantial sum of money to purchase the business. Funding can come in many forms, so look at the chapter on funding and explore all of the options. Because it is a larger sum of money, your personal assets will be more at risk than before. However, there is more of a guarantee that there will be a regular income coming into the business and more likely to provide you with immediate full time work, rather than you having to wait to build up a client list.

There are many advantages to buying an existing business including;

* Investors are more likely to provide finance for a business that is already making money

* The business has already been established, so no hard ground work to do

* It already has an established local patient list

* Any employees within the business will have knowledge of how the business is run

The disadvantages will need to be considered at the same time as the advantages;

* A larger amount of money will be needed to invest in an established business

* There may be unexpected expenses on faulty or out of date equipment, or premises repairs

* Staff who transfer with the sale of the business may not be happy or comfortable working for someone else, especially if you implement a different way of working

* If the business has been running inefficiently, what impact will it have on your future trading?

When buying an existing business, you will need the last three years financial information from the sellers Accountants, as well as looking at the current years unfinished accounts. What loans or HP repayments are still outstanding? You take over any debts as well as any assets. Find out how long the seller has been trading and what changes they have implemented over the years. You will also need to know how long is remaining on a lease or what the rental terms are and whether they are likely to be changed soon.

Take the accounts to your own Accountant to get their advice on whether it would be a viable investment. You will then need to show them to your Bank Manager or investors, together with your business plan relating to the business you wish to buy. If you get approval, legal documents will need to be drawn up to make the sale of business complete. In the contract you should also include a restriction on the current owner from setting up another practice within a specified distance. This reduces the risk of patients leaving you and following the previous owner to another practice, resulting in a diminished business.

Buying an existing business does take out some of the uncertainty of starting a new business. You and your advisers have to decide whether or not the existing business is worth taking over and if it has a viable future.

Valuing a Business

How do you know that the price you are paying when buying a business is fair and reasonable? Obviously, the vendor wants to get as much as possible from selling the business, but you want to pay as little as possible.

An accountant can help value a business for you. Their valuation is based on a number of things including;

* How long the business has been established

* What its current turnover and profit is

* What assets it currently has

* What value of stock the practice has

* The length and value of lease remaining

* What outstanding debts or expenses it has

* The reason the owner is selling

* Current state of the local market

* What the projected growth or turnover would be

* How full the diary currently is

* Experience of the present staff

To get an idea of how the business is performing, as well as the local market, talk to the vendor and the businesses existing patients. It is not in the vendor's interests to lie or exaggerate about the business, as you are allowed full access to the vendor's accounts.

Often if you are buying a practice, the details of what is included in the price will include a word called 'Goodwill.' This is a term used to describe anything other than all the fixtures, fittings, length of lease left or anything tangible. What it does refer to is the reputation, existing patients and loyalty of those patients to visit the practice.

This is very difficult to put a value on but should be based on,

* The reputation of the business

* The volume of patients who have, or currently do, visit the practice

A business is often valued at a multiple of earning or future earnings, taking into account any assets a business has, especially property.

Once you have established a valuation for a business you should then make an offer. A specific period of time called due diligence is then given for you to verify all the facts you have been given about the business. The price will probably then be negotiated until both parties agree on a final price.

Buying a Franchise

Franchises are not something often associated with Podiatry, but within the last year they have begun to be available. Buying a Franchise is about using a proven formula, branding and business experience to help you develop a successful business. The Franchiser will guide the Franchisee (you) in all aspects of starting up their business, using their own successful model of business as a frame. You will however have to strictly adhere to the Franchisers methods and branding as well as offering the same services which they provide. There may be differences in the way you want to do things or promote yourself to those that the Franchiser recommends, so you may not achieve the freedom you crave.

The Franchisor will charge you an initial start up fee for providing you with all the support and equipment, together with a monthly fee which is either fixed or a percentage of your turnover. Although this costs you money every month, it is in the Franchisors interest to help make the business a success so their income is as high as possible, as well as yours.

The start up fee often includes training, all equipment, stationary, building improvements, reception furniture, in fact everything you will need to start a business. A franchise agreement will be for a fixed period, after which you can either renew the agreement or sell the business on.

A Franchise is not suitable for all, so do some homework on the reputation of the brand and the people behind it. Don't forget that you will have to conform to their idea of a Podiatry practice, not yours. Check the franchise agreement thoroughly or seek legal advice before signing.

8 Commercial Mortgages

If you have decided to buy premises to work from you will need to borrow a substantial amount of money. This comes in the form of a commercial mortgage. It works very similar to a domestic mortgage that you would have for your own home, but is a debt which the business has to support. There are different lenders that you can get a commercial mortgage from and many factors to consider before you proceed with one. A Commercial mortgage is available from most Banks and Building Societies.

A commercial mortgage will be paid over a period of 15 years or more, and if you fail to keep up repayments, the property can be repossessed and you will not be able to trade from there. You will need to prove to the lender that you have a good credit rating and the business has potential to meet the costs or is already doing so if you are expanding or taking on an existing business.

To get the best advice to suit yourself and your particular needs, you should appoint a Solicitor and Chartered Surveyor.

Don't forget, that buying property is a good long term investment for the business, although it is a heavy financial liability.

When approaching a lender you will need to be prepared to show that the business is viable. Take with you; if you have them, the last two years audited accounts, your projected finances for the next year, bank statements, and your personal asset statement from your business plan, as well as your CV and Business Plan. If you are buying an existing business, the lender will require additional information relating to the businesses accounts, market, assets the business already has as well as its debts.

You will need to provide a deposit of between 20 − 35% of the value of the property. A lender will not provide you with anything more than an 80% mortgage for a commercial property, so you will need to find other ways of funding the deposit.

Although Banks and Building Societies are the obvious choice for discussing your mortgage requirements, there are other options open to you. Specialist lenders are available online and may be able to offer you a better deal. Arranging a mortgage yourself could also save you money. There are many finance websites that trawl through all the commercial mortgages on your behalf, including http://oppc.decision-finance.co.uk/commercial_mortgages_guide.html

Brokers are also available who will be able to give you independent advice on the whole range of mortgages that are available, rather than a bank only being able to offer their own products. A Broker will also monitor your mortgage after you have it in place to constantly check to see if you can get a financially better deal elsewhere. Brokers tend to work in a specific area of business, so if you decide to use one, make sure they understand your needs. You will probably have to pay a Broker a fee or commission as well as the mortgage arrangement fees which are paid to the lender. You will be able to find a commercial finance broker on the website of the National Association of Commercial Finance Brokers (NACFB). The web address is included in Appendix B.

Where ever you decide to go for your mortgage, talk to someone about your needs and requirements before doing anything and get a good idea of the costs and fees involved.

The term of the mortgage is decided by the lender and will almost always be less than a 25 year domestic mortgage. They will also set a fixed or variable interest rate, which is often 1% - 5% above the Bank of England base rate, as you are classed as a high risk borrower.

As with a domestic mortgage the type of mortgage can be a Repayment Mortgage, Interest Only Mortgage or Endowment Mortgage. For businesses there is another additional type call a Pension Plan Mortgage:

* **Repayment Mortgage** – you make payments each month which are made up of a portion of the mortgage and Interest accrued on the mortgage. At the end of the term the mortgage and all interest has been repayed.

* **Interest Only Mortgage** – you only make payments each month to cover the interest. At the end of the term you still owe the original sum, so you will need to prove that you are

paying into an insurance or pension which will have sufficient funds in it at the end of the mortgage term to pay off the outstanding mortgage.

* **Endowment Mortgage** – you pay every month a fixed amount into an investment which should then cover the mortgage and interest at the end of the term. This is a particularly risky option as it depends on the performance of the stock markets.

* **Pension Plan Mortgage** – you pay into a pension fund each month which then repays the mortgage at the end of the term.

Not only is repaying the mortgage back a costly affair, but the fees involved in arranging the mortgage can also be quite steep, and may effect which product and lender you choose.

Fees often include, but may vary between lenders;

* **An arrangement fee** – this is what your lender charges you for arranging the mortgage. This may be a set amount, but could also be a percentage based on the mortgage.

* **Valuation Fee** – because the lender is taking a risk by lending you such a large sum of money, they will request a valuation of the property. They may also insist on a Structural Survey.

* **Redemption Fee** – this is a penalty you will have to pay to the lender if you pay off the mortgage sooner than the specified term.

* **Legal Fees** – for using solicitors who dealt with the legal aspects of purchasing the property.

9 Funding a New Business

Now that you have decided to start a business you will need to find ways of funding it. If you are buying property you will need to arrange a commercial mortgage, but if you are not buying, you will need to raise enough capital to pay for your equipment, supplies, advertising, stationery, rent or lease, repairs or maintenance of property, decorating of practice, staff, insurance etc., even before you can start trading.

There are many ways of obtaining finance. You can use your own money, or that of your family, or you can borrow from banks or investors. There are also awards, grants and loans to consider.

Before you can decide where you will go for the finance, you need to work out exactly how much you are going to require. If you have not done a business plan yet, now is an essential time to start. You will be able to see what you need to spend money on as well as what the ongoing costs are likely to be. A business plan will also help you to convince investors that you are serious and have done your research. Whoever lends you money is going to want to know that their money is safe and will get repaid at some point.

When you have a figure for the initial start up costs, a figure for your living expenses and the ongoing business costs for the first 6 months, you will have an idea of the cost of setting up your business.

The first person to talk about finance to is yourself. No one else is going to invest if you personally aren't prepared to put your own money on the line. Look at your savings, investments or assets that could generate some capital to put into the business. Your biggest asset is your house. Remortgaging your house could generate sufficient funds to start your business, but discuss this with others that live with you as it will affect them as well as your monthly repayments of the mortgage. Once the business is running successfully and at a profit, you can repay yourself the money you leant it. Self financing allows you to have flexibility in the investment, paying yourself back when you can and not with inflated interest added on.

Family members will often gladly support you if they can with a business venture. However, if it fails, your relationship with them may suffer. Even though they may be family, treat it as a business proposition. Present them with your business plan and discuss your requirements, as well as when you would intend to start paying them back. Family members are often more willing to provide you with an interest free loan, but if you do repay them back with interest, be aware that it may have tax implications for them, as it effectively becomes a profit making investment.

A bank will also probably lend you money to get a business up and running in the form of a loan. This will have to be repaid together with interest over a set period of time. A bank will need to see an up to date Business Plan, in order for them to assess whether or not it is a viable business for them to risk their money in. They are also more likely to give you a loan if you have invested some money in it yourself. Banks also offer overdraft facilities on your account, which should be arranged prior to using them to keep costs to a minimum. Because money won't flow in and out of your account at exactly the same time you may need to use an overdraft to pay creditors whilst you are still waiting to get paid. Overdrafts are a good short term way of funding the business, whilst only paying for them when you actually use them.

If you have access to an Accountant or financial advisor, get their advice before you sign any loan agreements, to make sure that they suit your needs.

You don't need to be tied to only one option of raising finance; you can combine several different sources at the same time. Even once the business is established, further funding may be required to expand the business or develop additional clinics or services.

Other types of funding and support

There are many other different forms of funding available, some of which won't require repaying. A lot of funding comes from local areas and businesses, but there are also opportunities to acquire national or EU approved funding.

For more information on what funding is available to you locally, contact Business Link or equivalent in your part of the country, their contact details can be found in Appendix B, as well as other contact details for awards and loans mentioned in this chapter.

Grants

Grants are cheap ways of raising capital. They are often available at a low interest rate, or even interest free, and as such they are often highly sort after, with stiff competition. As well as capital, they often come with business experience and advice.

A grant is awarded to a business for a specific future project, by local or national government, as well as schemes like The Prince's Trust or The Arts Council. Some grants are not repayable so you will have to prove that your project is worthy.

You will very rarely receive a grant for more than 50% of the project costs and you will have to prove that the rest of the money is going to be provided by yourself. The creation of new jobs could work in your favour when applying for a grant.

Loans

Loans are available from many different sources. Choose a reputable one with as low an interest rate as possible. You will have to repay loans together with interest.

Loans you may wish to consider;

* The Princes Trust Loan – available up to a maximum of £5,000 to individuals aged 18 to 30 who are currently unemployed and having difficulty obtaining funding elsewhere. You are also appointed a business mentor for the first three years.

Awards

A business award is given to a business that has shown excellent standards, innovating work or exceptional business awareness. You can enter for an award free of charge and winning it can help promote your business as well as inject cash prize money into it. There are many types of awards available, issued by the government and local businesses, so contact your local Business Link to find out which could be suitable for you.

Some Awards you may wish to consider include;

* Shell LiveWIRE Young Entrepreneur of the Year Award – for people aged 16 to 30 who have made outstanding achievements in business. You have the chance to win up to £10,000 and must have had a business up and running for between 3 and 18 months.

* Startups Awards – awarded to the best new businesses in 13 different categories. Awards of up to £5,000 available for businesses that have been trading for less than three years. You will need to submit a report, 1000 words long, explaining why you should be considered for the award.

10 Market Research

Market Research is a useful way of assessing and understanding your potential customers as well as your competition. By understanding the needs of your patients you are more likely to target and advertise more effectively, thereby gaining valuable business. As your business grows you will need to keep monitoring your competitors, so keep a note in your business plan about what services they are developing, what their pricing is, as well as what your patients think of the services of other Podiatrists. However, if your business is new and trying to establish whether or not a Podiatrist is required in the location you desire and if there are enough customers for your business to develop, you will need to do some market research.

Your potential customers

Find out as much as you can about your potential market. Some things you may need to ask are:

* What type of person is likely to use your practice?

* Can they afford to spend money on themselves?

* What age and gender is most likely to use your practice?

* Will their particular social class or lifestyle be relevant to your business?

* How many potential customers live in the area?

* Are they being provided with an adequate service already?

You will also need to consider the future. Are there likely to be more or less potential customers in the area in 5–10 years time? If the town has a growing reputation for students or popular nightlife, do you think there will be much call for your business in a few years? What have your competitors got lined up for the future and will it affect customers returning to you?

There are many things to consider when you look at market research for your practice, many answers you can find out by looking around the area and listening to other people's opinions, but there is also a lot of information available from other more official sources. Most of the research you will be able to find will be free of charge, but others you will need to pay for.

* Visit your local library. They will have reference information about the local area.

* Visit the governments statistics website (listed in Appendix B), which provides information on all aspects of the area you wish to set up practice in.

* Internet. Spend some time on the internet researching about the town you intend to have your business.

* Purchase information from commercial publishers of market reports. This can be costly and is often not worthwhile for a small business dealing with customers whose needs you can probably work out yourself.

* As you start to see patients, talk to them. Ask them what they need, and how your practice could improve to attract more business.

Your Competitors

Before you start a business and open your Podiatry practice, you need to assess your competition and whether or not there are sufficient patients in the area for your clinic to be successful as well.

Take the map you used earlier when deciding on a location for the practice, and mark on it where all the other local Podiatrists are by finding their addresses in the phone directories. Look at the location of the premises you are interested in working from again. Is it a sufficient distance from the other Podiatrists? You don't want to be working too close to another; it could harm your business.

Example

Mrs Brown gets recommended to you by her friend. Chances are she doesn't know your name, but her friend told her that you worked in the High Street, but there are two Podiatry clinics and she goes to the wrong one. You have lost a hard earned new patient. Don't allow yourself to loose patients so easily to other Podiatrists from recommendations that are misinformed.

Alternatively, you don't want to get confused for poor work received by a neighbouring Podiatrist just because he's also in the same road.

Other Podiatrists are classed as direct competitors. Indirect competitors may include hairdressing salons, beauty salons or complementary clinics, all of whom may provide pedicures. This may seem trivial, but at the end of the day they are still providing a service similar to yours and thereby taking some of your potential income. It may be worth checking the location of other clinics and finding out what it is they provide.

What you now need to do is contact the other Podiatrists and find out several pieces of information;

* How much do they charge for routine Podiatry?

* How long they allocate for each treatment?

* What other services they provide (i.e. Home visits, Nail Surgery, Biomechanics)?

* How many Podiatrists work there?

* Are they working everyday?

* What hours do they work?

So how would your clinic differ from your competitors? Why should patients come to you instead of them?

Look at what your competitors are providing, take the best bits out of it and do it better. If they're only treating patients for 20 minutes, you spend 30 minutes. Patients like to have value for money and they also like to feel you have given them a thorough treatment. To most patients, the time you spend with them is a direct reflection on the quality of service. The first thing they will say if they are unhappy with medical services is how short their appointment time was, so give them your time, they are paying for it. Look at fees and for your first year keep them 'appealing' and competitive. You can always adjust your fees later when your business has grown. Above all offer a comprehensive and good quality service.

Most patients are quite loyal and once they are being treated by a Podiatrist they usually stay with them unless they take a dislike to what you've done. So don't worry about trying to tempt patients away from other Podiatrists. Concentrate on getting your own patients. To do this you have to be better or more appealing to potential patients than the others. Effective advertising, which is discussed in detail later, is essential to let patients know you are there.

11 Equipping your Practice

Before you can think about working in a clinic, you will need to equip it. The equipment can be bought second hand by looking in your professional journal in the 'items for sale' section. Buying second hand is of course cheaper, but you may have costly repairs or maintenance to do immediately. You will also have to arrange and pay for the delivery from wherever it is you are buying them from, which could severely increase the cost.

The other alternative is buying brand new. If you contact a supplier and discuss your needs, they may allow you a discount of up to 17% or offer you interest free payment over one year or a low interest rate over two years. This makes costing a lot easier at the start and keeps your initial overheads low.

A list of equipment you may need in order to provide routine Podiatry is given on page 54. All of these items do not include VAT. Currently at 17.5%, it can considerably increase the amount of money you have to spend on top of the actual cost of the equipment. You may decide you don't need all of what is on the list, so alter it accordingly. Appendix B, lists all the different suppliers of equipment, so contact them and get up to date catalogues. Don't forget that you do not need to buy the most expensive equipment, you need to buy the equipment which best suits your clinic. If space is limited, choose your equipment wisely. Ask yourself what is really necessary and what are nice luxuries which won't actually benefit or alter the running of the practice. If it isn't essential, keep your cash.

Disposable supplies are also required and will need replacing on a regular basis. Buy things you are going to use and what you are already familiar with. Don't waste money in trying new products just yet. Save that for when you have settled into the business. A full list is given on page 54.

Essential Equipment

Patients Chair	£792 - £2500
Operators Chair	£95 - £550
Steriliser	£525 - £4458
Ultrasonic cleaner	£225 - £580
6 Sets of Instruments	£265 - £524
Work Trolley	£130 - £1495
Nail Drill	£495 - £1049
Adequate Lighting	£79 - £349
Debris Tray	£28
Dustpan and Brush	£45
Total price range	**£2,679 - £11,578**

Disposable Supplies

Non Sterile Gloves	Felts
Couch Roll	Tubefoam
Sterile Water	Surface Cleaner
Sterile Blades	Hand Cleaner
Tubegauze	Dry Dressings
Adhesive Tape	Wound Dressing
Pre treatment wipe	Wound Medicaments
Yellow Contamination Bags	Cotton Wool
Sharps Bin	Mouldable Silicone
Verrucae treatments	

Adjust this list to what you are familiar with using. The costs of all this stock varies between different suppliers so shop around. Some suppliers give you free delivery if you spend a certain amount. You will not need a comprehensive stock of disposables to start with, stick with the basics to get you going.

All of the equipment and stock we have looked at so far has been for providing a routine Chiropody service, but what about the other aspects of Podiatry?

Biomechanics Equipment

If you want to you can spend a fortune on equipment for Gait Analysis, but before you do, it may be more prudent to start with the basics and build on from that. If you start it this way, you will gain valuable experience as well as gradually allowing your reputation and therefore your client base to increase. The expenses will become more justified if you know you will get the use out of it.

Basic Biomechanics Kit	Price Range
Tractograph	£13 – £20
Goniometer	£10 – £18
Tape Measure	£2
Plaster of Paris Bandage	£2 – £3
Foam Impression Boxes	£1.50 – £2.50
Frelons or pre formed Insoles	£2.50 – £20
Felt	£13 – £16
Wedges	£1 – £2
PPT or Regen Sheets	£9 – £13
Lower Limb Skeleton or foot skeleton	£43 – £426
	£97 – £522.50

Once again, adjust this list to what you would normally use, or what you are comfortable with, we all work differently.

A basic Biomechanics kit is not too expensive, but you will need to keep quite a large stock of different sized Frelons or preformed insoles to use as temporary or trial insoles. A lower limb skeleton is very useful to explain problems to patients, so they can see how it relates to themselves. Alternative and cheaper variations to the skeleton are posters which show muscles, bones and joints.

Once you start treating patients you will need to establish a relationship with a laboratory who will make your orthotics. There are several addresses in Appendix B for you to contact, all of which will usually supply you with prepaid boxes to transport the negative plaster of Paris casts to them. When deciding on a laboratory, you should look at costs, quality and turnaround time. Talk to colleagues who may already use a laboratory and see which they recommend.

If you decide to make the insoles or orthotics yourself in your own lab, you will need to be CE registered. This is a European Standard for Medical Devices such as Insoles or Orthotics. You do not need to be CE registered for making chair side insoles though. To become CE registered, contact the Medical Devices Agency who will send you the relevant forms and information. Be aware that if you are making your own insoles or orthotics, using grinders, glues and plaster of Paris, there are also lots of health and safety issues you will need to adhere to.

Progressing onto the secondary Biomechanics Kit provides you with a wonderful demonstration tool. Patients can now see what you see, when looking at them walking or running. Freeze framing images and using software to show angles etc. is great for sending impressive and informative reports to GPs and Consultants. But again, you have got to understand what you're looking at, so learn how to interpret what you see.

A bench top grinder can be very useful for doing minor adjustments to insoles or orthotics without having to send them back to the laboratory, which would mean patients are without their insoles whilst the adjustments are being completed.

Secondary Biomechanics Kit	Price Range
Treadmill	£700 – £2500
Lap Top Computer	£600 – £1500
Picture/Video Analysis Software	£500 – £1000
Digital Camcorder	£300 – £900
Bench Top Grinder	£700 – £1000
	£2800 – £6900

If you are going to posses the advanced kit, you will have to justify the expense. Specific Gait Analysis assessments would have to come at a greater charge for patients. You could also hire out the equipment for use to the local surgeons and consultants. A CAD CAM can be used instead of plaster of Paris casting to order custom made orthotics.

All this equipment is very impressive, but don't loose site of the fact that good diagnostic skills are still essential and form the basis of a good practitioner.

Advanced Biomechanics Kit	Price Range
Gait Analysis Equipment - In shoe pressure sensors - Pressure plates CAD CAM	£4,500+ £5,000+ **£9,500+**

Diabetic Equipment and Supplies

However you decide to provide a Diabetic service, you will need some additional pieces of equipment and a range of wound dressings for different types of ulcers.

Additional Diabetic Equipment	Price Range
Doppler	£330 – £580
Neurothesiometer	£1,000
Monofilaments	£13 – £14
Hammers	£5 – £18
Tuning Fork	£19 – £75
Sphygmomanometer	£49 – £95
Education and Advice leaflets	£0 – £4
	£1,416 – £1,786

As you can see, setting yourself up to provide Diabetic Assessments can be costly, so first look carefully to see if there is going to be a market for it. As high risk patients, Diabetics are often well catered for in the NHS.

Contact some of the Podiatry suppliers in Appendix B to obtain a basic range of wound dressings. The costs of dressings can be quite high, as some patients may require several wounds dressing at regular intervals. If wounds or ulcers need regular dressing, contact the patients GP and ask for the assistance of the practice nurse and arrange for it to be redressed by them.

If you are going to provide a Diabetic Service, consider writing reports to GPs or patients to keep them informed.

Domiciliary Equipment

The equipment and supplies you require to provide domiciliary visits are mainly what you would need when providing routine Podiatry in the clinic. You will need additional sets of instruments as well as a domiciliary case to carry everything in. A Domiciliary case will vary in price from £130 to £200, but try to pick one which is as lightweight as possible because when it is full of instruments and supplies it will be quite heavy. Don't forget to keep a supply of appointment cards with your telephone number for writing their next appointment on, or giving out as a point of contact for when they need to arrange a visit.

Nail Surgery Equipment

You will not require any major additional equipment except some different instruments and disposable supplies.

Equipment / Instruments	Price Range
Elevators	£6 - £7
Thwaites Nippers	£35 - £38
Forceps	£3 - £6
Scissors	£11 - £12
TG Applicator (Small)	£4
TG Applicator (Large)	£4
Scalpel Handle	£3
Syringe	£24 - £34
Resuscitation Mask	£6
TOTAL PRICE RANGE	**£96 – 114**

Supplies	Price Range
Local Anesthetic	£12 - £13
Needles	£8 - £11
Sterile Dressing Pack	£1 - £2
Sterile Cotton Wool	£3
Sterile Gauze	£1

Sterile Gloves	£0.50 - £1
Sterile Drapes	£1 - £2
Tornicots (S,M,L,XL)	£2
Dressings	£1 - £8
Face Mask	£11
Apron	£3
Phenol	£80
TOTAL PRICE RANGE	**£123.50 - £137**

Consider buying at least two sets of instruments in case you have 2 patients following each other that are booked in for surgery. One set can then be sterilized whilst you are using the other.

Most of the supplies listed above come in bulk packs. Divide the packs up to give yourself an idea of the individual costs when you are working out how to price your service.

Local Anesthetic is available to purchase from suppliers, but they should request a certificate of qualification that enables you to administer Anesthetics before they allow you to buy it.

This is just a list of equipment for the actual clinic for you to provide treatments, but what about the waiting area? You will need a desk, seating for patients and staff, and stationary. Desks and seating can be obtained from office supply companies or second hand from a local office furniture retailer. If your appointments are going to be kept on a computer then you will need to purchase the software to run the diary on as well as the computer.

Stationary will need to be printed before you open so that you are ready for patients. A list of typical stationary may include;

Stationary and Paperwork Requirements

Patient Assessment Sheet	Mileage Form
Patient Treatment Sheet	Business Cards
Neurovascular/Diabetic/Biom	Appointment Cards
echanics Assessment Sheet	Clinic Cash Book
Nail Surgery / Consent Forms	Bank Account Cash book
Headed Paper	Reception Diary
Patient Referral Sheet	Personal Diary
Accounting Sheet	Cash flow Book
Receipt Book	

Examples of some of these stationary are included in Appendix C, which you may copy for your own use.

12 Suppliers and Stock

To run an effective practice you will need to maintain a certain amount of stock so that you can treat multiple numbers of patients without repeatedly reordering. The amount of stock that you keep and manage on your premesis at one time is called Stock Control or Inventory control. Your stock is classed as every item you have which you use to produce or provide your service. Managing your stock control will result in good financial control, as not all of your money will be tied up in stock waiting to be used on patients. You should also have enough stock held in the clinic to be able to provide a service to patients, even if there is a problem with your supplier not being able to immediately provide the stock you need.

You will need to work out how much stock you are going to need to treat a specific number of patients. This is relatively easy for some items as you will probably use one item per treatment, but other supplies you may not need for everyone, just the odd patient. Nethertheless you have got to make sure that you have the stock in the clinic just in case a patient needs something out of the ordinary.

Although keeping a small amount of stock on the premesis will reduce the amount of storage space you will need, you may quickly run out of the basic supplies. Most Suppliers will deliver on the next day if you order before a certain time, but what if they can't fill the order for another week? Fortunately, most of the stock you will need is relatively cheap, so you should be able to afford to keep a certain amount on the premesis.

Too much stock will reduce the risk of you running out of supplies, but what about the shelf lives of certain products you buy? You will also have to find a lot of storage space to keep all this stock and your money is tied up waiting to be used on patients, and until it is, it is not generating any income.

Sometimes suppliers will gave discounts on bulk buying of certain products, this may be a good time to free up some capital to take advantage of the offer and save money. Make sure it is actually something you need and would use. If it isn't then don't buy it just because its on offer.

Suppliers

There is a list of suppliers in Appendix B, contact them for up to date catalogues. You will need a Supplier who offers you competative prices on the everyday supplies you need, as well as free or discounted delivery costs. They may produce their own brand of certain products which will be cheaper, but make sure they are of a comparable quality. The supplier needs to be reliable. If they let you down with a delivery, you are going to have to let down a patient, which reflects badly on your business.

Look for 30 days of interest free payment on all your purchases. When you have ordered some stock, the supplier should allow you 30 days in which to pay. Take advantage of this as it helps to maintain a healthy cashflow within your business.

When ordering large items such as equipment, contact different suppliers by telephone and talk to them about your requirements. Ask them what discounts they can offer, or if they can offer you interest free payments over a certain period of time. This is another good way of starting a business with very little capital, and can often be cheaper than obtaining a loan from a bank as the interest should be lower.

Sheffield-Made
Internationally acclaimed

From its modern manufacturing facility in Sheffield, Swann-Morton combines traditional blade-making skills with the latest technology to produce a comprehensive standard surgical range, together with specialised blades and an extensive disposable scalpel range.

All over the world, Surgeons, GPs, Nurses, Dentists, Chiropodists and Veterinary Practitioners rely on the consistent quality, precision and performance of Swann-Morton products.

All sterile products are irradiated in-house.

Swann-Morton®

PRECISION IN YOUR HANDS

Swann-Morton Limited,
Owlerton Green, Sheffield S6 2BJ, England.
Tel: 0114 234 4231 Fax: 0114 231 4966
e-mail: uksales@swann-morton.com
exportsales@swann-morton.com
www.swann-morton.com

$C\mathcal{E}$

All medical devices are
CE marked in accordance with
the Medical Device Directive
(93/42/EEC).

FM 73368

SGS

MADE IN SHEFFIELD

"Swann-Morton" and the "ring pattern logo" are the registered trade marks of Swann-Morton Limited and related companies.

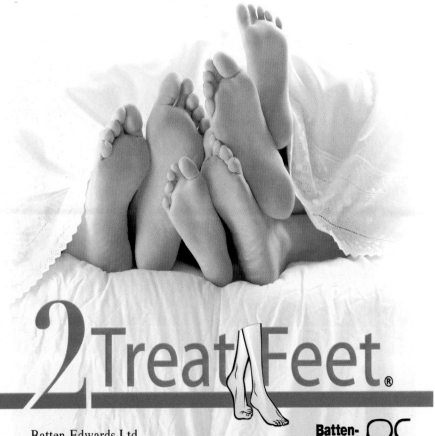

THE ONE PRODUCT SOLUTION FOR VERRUCAE AND FUNGAL INFECTIONS OF THE SKIN AND NAILS

Supplied to the profession for over 50 years

Economy size
bottle for the
surgery (Ref 351)

Spray bottle ideally suited for
use between toes (Ref 100)

Pipette applicator particularly
suitable for the treatment of nails.
(Ref 101)

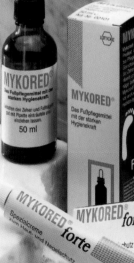

A special cream for dry,
scaly conditions of both
skin & nail (Ref 102)

Rigorously tested for
skin compatibility and
effectiveness

Nail Protection Oil
for flexibility & growth
(Ref 3303)

Hilary Supplies

34A Halstead Road, Mountsorrel, Loughborough, Leics LE12 7HF
Tel: 0116 230 1900 or Local Rate: 0845 3451678 Fax: 0116 230 3363
email: soniak@hilarysupplies.co.uk

Also now distributed by **canonbury** and **DLT**
healthcare

Has your new, *bigger* equipment catalogue arrived?

To receive your catalogue call us now on **01280 706661** and we'll rush one to you.

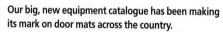

Our big, new equipment catalogue has been making its mark on door mats across the country.

Inside you'll find the very latest treatment couches, operator chairs, ultrasound and interferential devices, storage units and treatment lighting.

When you choose Canonbury as your healthcare equipment supplier you get high quality, proven products and a lot more:

● Free equipment consultancy ● A huge range to view in our Brackley showroom ● Service from our Area Managers nationwide ● A range of payment options that enable you to spread the capital cost over the life of the product* ● A dedicated Service Department to ensure you continue to get value from your investment into the future.

For strappings, bandages, massage creams and other consumables ask for our *Essentials* catalogue.

canonbury
healthcare

2 St James Road, Brackley, Northants NN13 7XY │ **T** 01280 706661 **F** 01280 706671 **E** info@canonbury.com **www.canonbury.com** order online *anytime*

* Subject to status.

Our Quality Your Confidence Our Quality Your Confidence

www.baileyinstruments.co.uk

527 Wilbraham Road,
Chorlton-cum-Hardy, Manchester M21 0UF
Telephone: +44 (0)161 860 5849
Fax: +44 (0)161 860 6353

e-mail: sales@baileyin.u-net.com

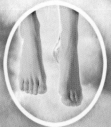

STEP IN FRONT
THE SMALL BUSINESS UPDATE

Step In Front, is the only quarterly update newspaper for the small business. It helps you to fit the pieces of the jigsaw together, to lay the foundations for a successful business as well as developing it for the future.

Articles include :

- ▶ Updates on current legislation
- ▶ New and innovative ideas on promotion and advertising
- ▶ Additional information not included in our small business books
- ▶ Impartial reviews of services provided by Business Banks
- ▶ National and International information which may be relevant to your business
- ▶ And much more.....

Published quarterly in folded A3 newspaper format
To subscribe to Step In Front, send a cheque made payable to Step Ahead Publications for £15.00, together with your name and address, to 10 Highpoint Business Village, Henwood, Ashford, Kent. TN24 8DH

STEP AHEAD
PUBLICATIONS

www.stepaheadpublications.co.uk
Putting you and your business a step ahead of the competition...

13 Costing your services

In your business plan you included the cost of providing a routine treatment to a patient and worked out how much profit you would make per person. But what about the other services you may want to provide? How much should you charge for them?

Biomechanics Service

There are different types of charges in Biomechanics for different things. Adapt the charges according to your Personal Survival Budget, your competition and the value of the service you are providing. Don't forget that you are providing a specialized service which you have spent a lot of money in training yourself and learning how to provide a thorough and professional service. You have also got to take into account that not all your appointments will be full, so the profit you make will allow for any gaps in your diary.

Example

The following price is based on a 1 Hour Biomechanical assessment using the basic Biomechanics kit, which may include a pair of chair side adapted Frelon Insoles, or a casting. On the following calculations, Bob decides to provide an hours biomechanical assessment for £40, making £11.01 profit per assessment.

Explanation of the table on page 72– It is very difficult to calculate what material you will use and how much it will cost. By breaking down packs and boxes into singular units you can estimate what the cost would be for one patient. The rent is based on working an eight hour day

Expenditure	Basis of calculation	Cost	Formulae
Possible Materials Used		£ 8 . 00	
Rent	Based on an 8 hour day costing £50 rent	£ 6 . 25	£50 / 8
Use of equipment	£137 assessment tools and educational model used over 1000 treatments	£ 0 . 14	£137 / 1,000
Personal Survival Budget	£5,990 per year, working a 24 hour week	£ 4 . 80	£5990 / 52 / 24
	Sub Total	**£ 19 . 19**	
Savings for Tax	17.5%	£ 7 . 00	£40 X 0.175
Savings for National Insurance	7%	£ 2 . 80	£40 X 0.07
	Total	**£ 28 . 99**	
	Profit per treatment	**£ 11 . 01**	£40 – 28.99

costing £50, so divide it into cost per hour. Wear and tear on equipment is an estimate. 1,000 assessments are approximately a life span of about 5 years in a practice perfoming a small number of assessments. Your Personal Survival Budget for the year will need to be divided into weeks, then the number of hours worked in that week. You will be taxed on the price you charge the patients, so budget for tax and National Insurance Contributions.

Example

The cost of casted orthosis from laboratories will vary depending on the quality and speed of production. The cost of the orthotic could also include the cost of fitting that orthotic in the patients shoe and thereby taking up some of your time in the clinic.

For Bob to supply a pair of casted orthotics to a patient and fit them, would cost him £114.83, so charging the patient £140 would create a profit of £25.17. Bob's profit would be greater if he only allowed 15 minutes for a fitting. His profit per orthotic would rise to £27.94.

Expenditure	Basis of calculation	Cost	Formulae
Rent	Based on an 8 hour day costing £50 rent	£ 3 . 13	£50 / 8 /2
Laboratories cost of manufacture		£ 75 . 00	
Personal Survival Budget	£5,990 per year, working a 24 hour week	£ 2 . 40	£5990 / 52 / 24 / 2
	Sub Total	**£ 80 . 53**	
Savings for Tax	17.5%	£ 24 . 50	£140.00 X 0.175
Savings for National Insurance	7%	£ 9 . 80	£140.00 X 0.07
	Total	**£ 114 . 83**	
	Profit per treatment	**£ 25 . 17**	£140.00 – 114.83

Explanation of the table – The rent is based on working an eight hour day costing £50, so divide it into the cost per hour, then divide again for half an hour. The cost of the device from the laboratories will depend on what materials it is made from. Your Personal Survival Budget for the year will need to be divided into weeks, then the number of hours worked in that week, then divided again for half an hour. You will be taxed on the price you charge the patients, so budget for tax and National Insurance Contributions.

Example

A 1 hours Gait analysis using the treadmill and PC software could be quite costly. Being such a specialized area, patients would be willing to pay more because their expectations are higher. You will still use some supplies to provide the patient with a chair side orthotic or casting.

If you were to charge £70 for a gait analysis assessment, costing £41.20, you would make £28.80 profit.

Expenditure	Basis of calculation	Cost	Formulae
Possible Materials Used		£ 8 . 00	
Rent	Based on an 8 hour day costing £50 rent	£ 6 . 25	£50 / 8
Use of equipment	£5000 analysis tools and equipment used over 1000 treatments	£ 5 . 00	£5000 / 1,000
Personal Survival Budget	£5,990 per year, working a 24 hour week	£ 4 . 80	£5990 / 52 / 24
	Sub Total	£ 24 . 05	
Savings for Tax	17.5%	£ 12 . 25	£70.00 X 0.175
Savings for National Insurance	7%	£ 4 . 90	£70.00 X 0.07
	Total	£ 41 . 20	
	Profit per treatment	£ 28 .80	£70.00 – 41.20

Explanation of the table – Calculate roughly what the cost of materials could be for the hour. The rent is based on working an eight hour day costing £50, so divide it into cost per hour. Wear and tear on equipment is an estimate. 1,000 assessments are approximately a life span of about 5 years in a practice performing a regular number of assessments. Divide your Personal Survival Budget for the year into weeks, then hours. Add the tax and National Insurance Contrications based on your fee to the patient.

Diabetic Service

Example

Bob decides to provide a Diabetic Assessment only service which takes 30 minutes, and may require report writing. Bob decides to charge £20 for a half hour assessment of a Diabetic patient. Taking into account the cost of providing the service he would make £8.07 profit per assessment.

Expenditure	Basis of calculation	Cost	Formulae
Rent	Based on an 8 hour day costing £50 rent	£ 3 . 13	£50 / 8 / 2
Use of equipment	£1500 assessment tools and equipment used over 1000 treatments	£ 1 . 50	£1500 / 1,000
Personal Survival Budget	£5,990 per year, working a 24 hour week	£ 2 . 40	£5990 / 52 / 24 / 2
	Sub Total	£ 7 . 03	
Savings for Tax	17.5%	£ 3 . 50	£20.00 X 0.175
Savings for National Insurance	7%	£ 1 . 40	£20.00 X 0.07
	Total	£ 11 . 93	
	Profit per treatment	£ 8 .07	£20.00 – 11.93

Explanation of the table – The rent is based on working an eight hour day costing £50, so divide it into cost per hour, then half hour. Wear and tear on equipment is an estimate. 1,000 assessments are approximately a life span of about 5 years in a practice perfoming a small number of assessments. Divide your Personal Survival Budget for the year into weeks, then hours, then half hour. Add the tax and National Insurance Contricutions based on your fee to the patient.

Domiciliary Visits

Example

Bob's Personal Survival budget is £5,990 per year, working a 24 hour week. If he allows 30 minutes for a routine treatment, 15 minutes traveling time to the patient and 15 minutes traveling away from the patient, he is effectively spending 1 hour of his time providing a home visit.

Mileage and wear and tear on Bob's vehicle is based on a cost per mile of around 52p. Assuming an average mileage of 10 miles per patient. The supplies used for a patients treatment are minimal, but the use of the equipment also needs to be taken into account.

Bob decides to charge £25 for a home visit so should be able to make £7.73 profit per treatment assuming he only spends 30 minutes at their home.

Expenditure	Basis of calculation	Cost	Formulae
Vehicle Expenses	52p per mile for 10 miles	£ 5 . 20	52p X 10
Supplies		£ 1 . 00	
Use of Domiciliary Bag	£200 bag used over 2000 treatments	£ 0 . 10	£200 / 2,000
Use of instruments	£70 set of instruments over 2000 treatments	£ 0 . 04	£70 / 2,000
Personal Survival Budget	£5,990 per year, working a 24 hour week	£ 4 . 80	£5990 / 52 / 24
	Sub Total	£ 11 . 14	

Savings for Tax	17.5%		£ 4 . 38	£25.00 X 0.175
Savings for National Insurance	7%		£ 1 . 75	£25.00 X 0.07
		Total	**£ 17 . 27**	
		Profit per treatment	**£ 7 . 73**	£25.00 – 17.27

Explanation of the table – Although there is no rent to include when providing a Domiciliary visit, there are other additional costs. The cost per mile for using your car can be found on HM Revenue and Customs website. Wear and tear on bag and instruments is over an estimated 2,000 treatments which is approximately a life span of about 5 years in a practice doing around 30 home visits per month. Divide your Personal Survival Budget for the year into weeks, then hours. Add the tax and National Insurance Contricutions based on your fee to the patient.

Nail Surgery Service

Don't forget that not all Podiatrists can perform nail surgery, and some who can, decide not to, so you are providing a specialized service. Your price should reflect the value of having surgery. Don't undervalue the importance of your skills which enable you to perform minor nail surgery. Increase your charge for a total nail avulsion slightly, although there are very few additional things to buy when performing a total rather than a partial operation. There may be additional dressings required, or it may take slightly longer to heal, so consider adding on the costs of an additional 30 minutes of your time for another visit by the patient to the clinic to get it checked.

Example

Look at the cost of disposable supplies you will require to perform one partial nail avulsion. Then consider the amount of your time that the patient will take up. If you allocate one hour for one operation followed by 3 appointments over the next few weeks to redress and check the wound, they could, in effect be taking up to the equivalent of 2.5 hours of your time. Also include the use of the equipment, assuming they have of life span of 2000 treatments, as well as dressings you provide for the patients to redress the wound at home.

The following costs are based on one partial nail avulsion operation, charged at £150.

Expenditure	Basis of calculation	Cost	Formulae
Dressings for patients		£ 5 . 00	
Supplies		£ 14 . 00	
Use of instruments	£114 set of instruments used over 2000 treatments	£ 0 . 06	£114 / 2,000
Rent	Based on an 8 hour day costing £50 rent	£ 15 . 63	£50 / 8 X 2.5
Personal Survival Budget	£5,990 per year, working a 24 hour week	£ 12 . 00	£5990 / 52 / 24 X 2.5
	Sub Total	£ 46 . 69	
Savings for Tax	17.5%	£ 26 . 25	£150.00 X 0.175
Savings for National Insurance	7%	£ 10 . 50	£150.00 X 0.07
	Total	£ 83 . 44	
	Profit per treatment	£ 66 . 56	£150.00 – 83.44

Explanation of the table – Providing patients with dressings should be budgeted into your costings together with the individual costs of all the disposable supplies required. The rent is based on working an eight hour day costing £50, so divide it into cost per hour, then multiply it by the total time included for the operation and after care. Do the same to work out your Personal Survival Budget for the total time. Wear and tear on equipment is an estimate. 2,000 operations are approximately a life span of over 20 years in a practice perfoming a couple of operations a month. Add the tax and National Insurance Contricutions based on your fee to the patient.

14 Employing Staff

If you have decided to rent a room, the services of staff should be included in your rent. However, if you have taken on a leasehold or freehold property, you will probably need to employ reception staff together with cleaners. In the future you may even wish to employ another Podiatrist to work with you if you have too much work for yourself to cope with.

At the start of a business you may have to consider employing staff. To reduce costs you could clean the premises yourself every night, but covering a reception desk whilst trying to treat patients is not as simple. It looks unprofessional to keep stopping a treatment to answer the telephone, leave it on answer phone or have the reception area unmanned, so you may have to have clerical assistance.

When you employ someone full or part time you have certain responsibilities and obligations to your staff.

* You must provide them with a contract of employment outlining the terms and conditions of employment.

* You will have to provide a pay statement outlining their pay and any deductions that have been taken off.

* They have a right to work in a safe working environment which meets minimum working conditions.

* You will need to arrange insurance for illness or injury of employees as a result of working for you.

* HM Revenue and Customs will need to be contacted. You must register as an employer and set up a payroll, as well as forward any tax and National Insurance Contributions your

employee needs to pay.

* Paid Holiday, working hours and rest breaks for employees need to be taken into account.

* You must pay at least the National Minimum wage.

* Some staff may be entitled to Statutory Sick Pay if they have been off sick for more than three days.

* If an employee becomes pregnant or has become a parent, they are entitled to maternity, paternity or adoption leave and parental leave during the first five years of the child's life.

* You cannot discriminate between employees.

Contract of Employment

Once you have someone who fits the criteria for your job and they have accepted the position, you will need to draw up an employment contract. This can be in the form of an oral, written or implied contract. Even if you do not issue a written contract, an oral contract is just as binding and you as the employer are still under the legal obligations expected from an employer. However, a written statement of the job, including the duties and terms and conditions of the position, should legally be drawn up within two months of starting.

Having a written contract or statement, is the clearest way for both parties to understand what is expected of them and may prevent problems or disagreements arising in the future.

An example of an employment contract is included in Appendix D, made with the assistance of Business Link. On their website, you can complete your own employment contract which has been checked by Business Link Lawyers.

Your contract must include the legal name of the employer and employee, together with a date when the employee started work. The employees pay must be stated as well as the hours of work and holiday entitlement. Terms of sick pay should be included. There should also be a description of the work you will expect them to undertake and where this work will be performed. How long is the employment for? If there is a fixed date when the employment will end, state it in the contract, as well as the length of notice required by either party to terminate employment. If you intend to pay into a pension scheme on behalf of your employee, this must be included in the contract. It must also contain dismissal, disciplinary and grievance procedures which should meet statutory minimum requirements.

Although these are particulars specific to the job you are providing, there are also implied terms within an employment contract. It is taken for granted that a safe environment is being provided and that the employee will be honest, trustworthy and practice confidentiality for patients. Your employees automatically have the right to paid holidays and the National Minimum wage.

If you need to change an employee's contract, you must inform the employee and get their written consent and agreement to the changes. If you do not, you will be vulnerable to litigations by the employee for breach of contract.

Tax and National Insurance Contributions

When you become an employer, the biggest obligation you have is regarding your employees' tax and National Insurance Contributions. When they join you, the employee must provide you with a P45, which should have been supplied by their previous employer if they had one, and their National Insurance (NI) Number.

You will need to keep HM Revenue and Customs informed when you take on an employee. The contact details are in Appendix B. Ask them for the 'New Employers Starter Pack' which they will send you together with a CD ROM, to guide you through the calculations needed to work out an employees income tax and National Insurance Contributions, as well as being able to keep a record of all payments and deductions.

You will also be issued with an Employer Reference Number, which will need to be quoted on official forms.

Other forms in the Starter Pack Include;

* P11 – Deductions working sheet to record your employees pay details.

* P32 – Employer's Payment Record. A record of details of every time you make a payment.

* P45 – This form is given when an employee leaves work.

* P46 – Employer's notice to Tax Office – this form is used when the employee does not have a P45.

* P49 – Paying someone for the first time – this booklet is used to work out how to deduct National Insurance contributions and PAYE Income Tax

Completing a P45

Your employee will bring with them a P45 from their previous job. They must keep Part 1A, whilst you need Parts 2 and 3. Make sure there is a valid National Insurance Number containing two letters, six numbers followed by an A, B, C or D. If the employee does not know their NI Number you can trace it by completing the form CA6855, which is on the Starter Pack CD ROM.

Complete section 3 of the P45 by adding your Employer reference number, which is given to you in your starter pack.

You will then need to set up a payroll record for the employee, using the details from the P45, so that you can record their pay and deductions.

Once you have a completed P45, keep Part 2 safe and send Part 3 to HM Revenue and Customs. Part 1 is kept by the employee.

When someone leaves your employment, you must provide them with a P45 for them to take to their new employer.

PAYE

'Pay As You Earn.' This is applied to all payments which an employee receives by working for you, including Statutory Sick Pay and Maternity Pay.

Look for your employees Tax code on their P45, then use this code, together with the tax pay tables included with your New

Employers Starter Pack, to calculate the amount of tax your employee should pay. Keep records of all the pay and deductions relating to your staff.

You will need to provide a wage slip every month to your employee to show how their pay has been calculated and what deductions have been included. You can create your own wage slip, as long as it contains the following information;

* The gross amount of pay for that period

* Details of deductions

* The net amount of pay after deductions

* Method of payment to the employee

At the end of every tax year, you will need to issue your staff with a P60. This is a form which details the total amount of tax that has been deducted for the whole year.

When you are processing an employees pay, you need to know how to calculate tax deductions and allowances. Every 19th day of the month, or 22nd if it is by electronic payment, you will need to make your payment to HM Revenue and Customs of the deductions you have taken from your staffs wages. If this is less than £1,500 they may allow you to pay quarterly.

Paid Holiday

From the first day an employee starts work they are entitled to paid holiday. They do not have to work for you for a certain period before holiday is allowed. For each week they have off, they are entitled to payment for that week based on the paid hours they would normally work.

In the contract you should specify what the length of holiday your employee will be entitled to and when the leave year begins. All employees are entitled to four weeks paid holiday a year. If you are employing a part time member of staff, their holiday is calculated on a pro rata basis. For example, if a part time employee works three quarters of the hours of a full time then they will be allowed 3 weeks.

The number of weeks paid holiday a part time employee is entitled to can be calculated using the following formulae:

$$\frac{\text{Weekly hours of part time work}}{\text{Weekly hours of full time work}} \times 4 = \text{Number of paid weeks holiday per year}$$

If a member of staff joins part way through a year, they are entitled to paid holiday proportionate to the rest of that year.

Employees are not entitled by law to take pay instead of the time away from work. Due to health and safety, everyone must have time away from work, however if an employee has a certain number of unused days remaining at the end of the year, you may consider allowing them to carry those days over to the following year. The maximum number of days you allow an employee to carry over should be specified in the contract.

Bank Holidays and Public Holidays are left to employers' discretion. You can include them in your employees entitlement, or they may take them separately and unpaid. Regardless of whether an employee is part time or full time, they are entitled to exactly the same holiday entitlement and contract as each other.

When an employee requires taking some of their holiday, they must give notice. This notice period should be agreed within the contract, as agency staff or alternative staff arrangements may need to be made to cover that person's job.

You will need to specify if there are restrictions as to when your employee can take leave. You may decide that you will always close for the week between Christmas and New Year, so your staff will not be required to attend at that period either. They will need to know that part of their entitlement will be taken up on those set dates.

When a member of staff leaves your employment, they are entitled to proportionate pay for any holiday they have not received for that year. If someone has worked half the year then leaves, but has only taken one week's holiday in that time, they should be paid for the remaining one week which they have not taken. Because they have only worked half of the year, they are only entitled to two weeks holiday up to that point. Consequently, if they have taken more than their entitlement before they leave, you may make a deduction from their final payment to take this into account.

National Minimum Wage

Since April 1999, all workers in the UK have a legal right to a minimum wage to promote equality and fairness amongst employers. As of 1 October 2006, the Minimum wage was increased to £5.35 for employees over 22 years old. Those aged 18 – 22 receive £4.45 per hour, whilst 16 – 17 year olds receive £3.00 per hour. You are not entitled to the National Minimum Wage if you are classed as self employed or work as a voluntary worker.

Statutory Sick Pay

As an employer you must pay your employees sick pay when they are away from work because of illness. Within one period of time, Statutory Sick Pay is paid for a maximum of 28 weeks.

To qualify for sick pay an employee must;

* Notified you of their sickness within seven days.

* Be already employed by you and have already started working for you.

* Be over 16 year's old or less than 65 years old on the first day of sickness.

* Be ill for four or more days in a row.

* Have weekly earnings equal to or more than the lower earnings limit for National Insurance Contributions.

* Have earnings which you, the employer, are liable to pay Class 1 National Insurance Contributions.

Sick pay is based on the period of pay before the illness started and should include at least the previous two months. Average the monthly pay and divide into a weekly pay. This is what you will have to pay your employee each week that they are away from work.

Keep detailed records of when you have staff off, for how long and what Sick Pay was paid to them.

If your employee is not entitled to Statutory Sick Pay, but is incapable of work for at least four days in a row, you should provide them with form SSP1 (available from the Department of Work and Pensions) so they can claim incapacity benefit from their Social Security Office.

The payments you have made to your employee for Statutory Sick Pay can be claimed back from your National Insurance Contributions and PAYE payments. Alternatively you can contact your local HM Revenue and Customs Accounts office and inform them of the amount of Statutory Sick Pay you need to recover. The address for your local office will be on your pay slip booklet P30BC.

Statutory Maternity Pay

To qualify for Statutory Maternity Pay, your employee must earn on average no lower than the lower earnings limit for National Insurance Contributions. It is paid at a rate of 90 per cent of the average earnings for the first six weeks, and then 20 weeks paid at the standard rate of £108.85 per week, which is set by the government, or 90 per cent of the average weekly earnings, whichever is the lower.

As an employer, you can recover 92 per cent of payments made for Statutory Maternity Leave, by deducting it from the payments you make to HM Revenue and Customs. In April 2007, the government is intending to extend paid maternity leave to 39 weeks.

After maternity leave, your employee is entitled to return to the same job, hours and terms and conditions to those that were in place before she left. If an employee decides to take additional maternity leave, they are entitled to return to the same job, or a suitable alternative.

You will need to write and confirm the date when the employee will be returning to work, within 28 days of being informed of when the employee will start her maternity leave. They cannot return to work until at least two weeks after the baby has been born.

Fathers are entitled to Paternity Pay, as long as he has been working for 26 weeks, 15 weeks before the expected birth of the child and pay sufficient National Insurance Contributions. They are then entitled to two weeks paternity leave. Fathers who do not qualify for Paternity Pay may be entitled to Income Support.

An Employee is expected to give you 28 days notice of when they intend to start their Paternity Pay. It is paid at a rate of £108.85 per week or 90 per cent of weekly earnings, whichever is the lower. As is the case for Statutory Maternity Pay, you, the employer, can claim back 92 per cent of Paternity Pay by deducting it from your HM Revenue and Customs payments.

When adopting a child, one member of the couple is entitled to Statutory Adoption Pay, whilst the other receives Statutory Paternity Pay, so long as they have been working 26 weeks at the time they are told they have been matched with a child for adoption. Adoption leave can be for 52 weeks, of which 26 weeks is paid at £108.85 per week or 90 per cent of weekly earnings, whichever is the lowest, followed by 26 weeks unpaid leave.

Employing part time staff

By employing part time staff, you will be able to keep some of your costs as an employer down a little. Part time staff provide more flexibility for a business to adapt to the need for services and change as the business grows. You may find that employees are a lot happier and stress free because they are not trying to hold down a full time job. Happier staff are more likely to stay with you, thereby cutting down the cost of recruiting new employees and training them up for the job.

Employing part time staff will cause you to need more repetitive training for each individual employee. They will probably not earn enough or contribute enough to National Insurance Contributions to qualify for statutory sick pay, maternity pay or a state pension. Pay will need to be calculated on a pro rata basis, as may any other financial benefits such as private pension contributions.

Part time employees have the same rights as their full time colleagues so do not treat them any different, otherwise you could find yourself facing an employment tribunal. They must have pro rata contracts (in proportion to the hours they work in relation to a full time post) with comparable;

* Rates of pay

* Entitlement to holiday pay, sick pay and maternity leave.

●   Access to training.

Job sharing is a useful role to obtain cover for the reception desk. This involves two or more employees sharing the responsibility and pay of the reception on different days at different times.
This has the benefit of;

●   Providing flexible cover for the desk

●   Having the skills of more than one person for the same job.

●   Cover for the reception when one of the job sharer is ill or on holiday

●   Reduction of employee stress because of the shared work load

However, because job sharers will very rarely see each other as they work separate times or days, there may be a lack of continuity or a difference of opinions on how particular jobs should be performed.

Once again, it is much simpler and less costly to rent a room from someone else. Your overheads are going to be a lot less because all of the expenses are shared. Start by renting, you won't be able to afford all these additional expenses to start with, unless you are established or taking over an existing profitable business.

B

Managing Your Practice

15 Managing your Appointments

It may seem obvious, but don't forget to buy a diary for the reception as well as one for yourself. Decide what time you are going to start in the morning, what time you are going to be closed for lunch and what time you will finish. If you can stick to the same times every day, there's less chance that you will arrive in the morning to find patients waiting because they've been booked in without you knowing.

How long are you going to allow for each treatment? Are all new patients going to be allocated longer appointments to allow for the additional paper work? Most treatments will last about 30 minutes. Are you going to allocate a break in the morning and afternoon sessions, to catch up with paperwork, sterilise instruments or have a cup of tea?

Once you've decided all of this, you need to go through the reception diary putting in the days you are working together with the hours and available appointment times. You will also need to discuss this with all receptionists or whoever will be answering the telephone.

Receptionists will also need to know what you treat in case patients ask them a question over the phone, so provide a brief summary of your services to the receptionists together with the charges for treatment.

Another important decision you need to make is how you intend to collect the fees?

It is pointless, time consuming and expensive sending bills out by post to each person you treat, so collect it immediately after the treatments. Who will collect it? If the receptionists are going to collect it, how will they know what to charge each patient? Will you send them out with a receipt, so the receptionist knows what they've had done? Or will you accompany them to the reception and inform the receptionist? The other alternative is collecting the money yourself in your treatment room. Decide how it will work and again inform the receptionist. Either way you will need a float (a mixture of change) for when patients don't come with the exact money. A cash book is also handy to write down the patients name and how much they paid you, this will help with your accounting.

Charging for Non Attendance

Occasionally, patients will not attend for their appointments and you are left waiting for them and wasting an appointment which could have otherwise been filled.

If this happens you will need to decide whether or not you are going to charge the patient a non attendance fee. This is perfectly acceptable and is common practice with other health care professionals e.g. Dentists. Your fee should cover the costs of you physically being in the clinic for that appointment time.

Example

Based on Bob's Personal Survival Budget and the cost of the rent of the clinic for the 30 minutes wasted through non attendance, Bob has decided to charge a £10 fee.

Expenditure	Basis of calculation	Cost	Formulae
Rent	Based on an 8 hour day costing £50 rent	£ 3 . 13	£50 / 8 / 2
Personal Survival Budget	£5,990 per year, working a 24 hour week	£ 2 . 40	£5990 / 52 / 24 / 2
	Sub Total	**£ 5 . 53**	
Savings for Tax	17.5%	£ 1 . 75	£10 X 0.175
Savings for National Insurance	7%	£ 0 . 70	£10 X 0.07
	Total	**£ 7 . 98**	

Explanation of the table – The rent is based on working an eight hour day costing £50, so divide it into cost per hour, then per half hour. Your Personal Survival Budget for the year will need to be divided into weeks, then the number of hours worked in that week, then divided again into half hours. You will be taxed on the price you charge the patients, so budget for tax and National Insurance Contributions.

Send a letter to the person who did not attend for their appointment explaining about your policy to charge for wasted appointments and the demand for appointments. The patient will respond in one of three ways. The first is the nice way, they will send you your fee, admit they forgot the appointment, apologise and rebook. The second way is the patient who will grudgingly pay you the fee, complain and may or may not rebook. The third is complete non acceptance, you receive no fee, no contact from the patient and no rebooked appointment. Any of these ways are good for your business. If non attenders do not rebook, you are gradually filtering out all the bad patients leaving you with the good ones.

Don't bother to waste your time trying to chase up a £10 fee if the patient doesn't pay after the initial letter. Make a note of it in the patients record, and if they do happen to come again, you can ask them for it in person.

Use your discretion as to whether or not you should adhere to your fee for everyone. Maybe make exceptions for patients who have been coming for years without normally failing to attend, or those who have serious illness, family troubles etc.

On your appointment cards, add a line about charging for appointments which are not kept, so that you know that patients have been informed.

Accepting credit cards

Although most of your patients will probably be elderly and may not prefer to pay by credit cards, it is becoming culturally more accepted to pay for everything on credit cards, no matter how small the fee.

If you have decided to accept credit card payments you will need to contact your bank and arrange for the installation of a terminal, from which the credit card details are transmitted to the bank and the funds transferred into your account.

It does provide a quick and simple way to collect the fees, but you must be aware of the charges it incurs.

To start with, the bank will probably charge you a joining fee or set up charge, which is renewed every year. Alternatively there may be a monthly rental charge. In addition to this a percentage charge of each transaction is payable by you.

Example

Set up fee - £300
Transaction fee - 3%

If you have a full clinic of 14 patients, each paying £17 for treatment, the daily charge at 3% would be £7.14, if they all paid by credit card. In one month the charges in a full time practice could equate to £142.80 in addition to the set up fee or monthly rental charge as opposed to less than a pound for putting a similar amount of cheques and cash into your business bank account.

You have to decide whether or not accepting credit and debit cards is going to be financially beneficial for your business. Is it going to make patients come to you, rather than a competitor, just because you accept credit cards? Probably not. Because you will only be dealing in small amounts, most patients will probably have sufficient cash with them, or their cheque book.

One way around the charges for credit cards is to pass some of the fee onto patients. Explain that if they wish to pay by credit card a 3% charge will be added to their bill. Most people will probably not want to pay this fee and it could end up being a negative talking point between patients and therefore negative advertising.

If profits are tight, accepting credit cards is a luxury and not really essential.

16 Patient Record Systems

You are almost ready to start treating patients, but you must be prepared with all your stationery, and you will need to consider what format your patient records are going to be written and maintained in.

You are legally and professionally bound to keep records of patients' treatment, in case of litigation claims. Record keeping should be organised and tidy, with clear and legible entries. Use abbreviations recognised by your profession, so others can follow your treatment plans.

You can purchase some pre designed A5 patient cards from stationery suppliers, as well as Podiatry Suppliers, which can be filed in index boxes. The only trouble with this type of patient record system is that you will soon fill a box full of cards and will need numerous boxes to store all your patients details. If you receive letters about patients, they will undoubtedly be printed on an A4 sheet of paper. Folding this up and storing it in an index box, looks unprofessional and scruffy and eventually becomes detached from the records and gets lost.

An A4 filing system and stationery works much better. Keep patient records in a folder or clear sleeve with a fastening to keep it all together. Store the records in a secure, lockable filing cabinet.

The patient assessment sheet needs to contain patient details, together with contact information, as well as a note of where or how the patient got to know of you. This is important so that you can keep a check on where patients are hearing about you and what advertising is being effective and cost efficient. Record a list of referral sources on the patient referral sheet, keeping a tally over the year.

Patient assessment sheets also need to contain medical history, medication, allergies and operation history information. List the patient's main complaints and leave an area for a management plan.

If you wish to include it, you can design a form which has space for Neurovascular, Diabetic or Biomechanical assessments as well, although you may not use it for every patient and could end up being a waste of paper and printing costs. Separate forms would be more economical so you can use them when necessary.

A patient treatment sheet is also needed to record what treatment the patient received at each visit. Each entry on this sheet will need to be dated and signed.

Most of these forms can be simply designed on a home computer then photocopied, to keep costs to a minimum.

Electronic Record Keeping

As we progress into the 21st century, records and information is increasingly being stored on computors.

Systems are available which can offer;

* Patient records including Medical History, clinical notes, charts, diagrams and pictures.

* Abbreviations, terms and phrases dictionary

* Appointments in diary format

* Accounts

* Scheduling of reminders

* Back up support and training for users.

These types of software packages can be available from as little as £300, and many come with a 30 day free trial so you can see if the system is right for you.

If you are going to store electronic information about your patients, you will need to register with the Data Protection Registrar.

Data Protection

The Data Protection Act 1998, was formed to protect the freedom of patients and their right to privacy with respect to the processing of their personal data.

Because you will be keeping personal information about patients on records in either paper or electronic (computer) form you are subject to the Data Protection Act 1998.

Personal Information is anything which can be identified with a person, such as a name, address, or post code.

You will need to register with the Information Commissioner or Data Protection Registrar at the address in Appendix B. This will include registering yourself and the practice and does involve a small fee of £35 per year. Registration will also be necessary if you are keeping film or video recordings of a patient's gait analysis. Paper records need to be stored in a lockable and fire proof cabinet. Failure to register can result in a heavy fine.

Patients have the right to request access to their records under the Data Protection Act and Access to Medical Records Act 1990, although you can charge up to £10 to provide the information they request.

All entries in a patients record need to be in legible black ink and all entries, corrections or changes should be dated and signed.

Within the last few years, businesses have been subject to bogus data protection agencies scamming money from them. They will send a letter to you demanding payment of £95–£135 to register. Ignor any letters which are not sent from the Information Commissioners Office.

Retaining Records

You will need to make sufficient provision for patient records to be retained for certain periods of time in order to meet legal requirements.

All patient records should be retained for eight years after their last appointment.

Children's records should be retained until the patients twenty fifth birthday or eight years after their last appointment, whichever is longest.

17 Consent and Ethicises

When patients arrive for treatment, they should be fully aware of what is going to happen to them. If they have never had treatment before, they may feel a little apprehensive. Explain to them what you are going to do before you do it. If they verbally agree, then verbal consent is sufficient for treatment to continue. If they do not agree to your proposed treatment then you cannot go forward with it. Patients have every right to refuse consent, and you should not continue even if you feel it is in the patient's best interests.

Consent is necessary to provide the general public with information regarding their treatment so that they may make an informed choice, as well as protecting you from litigation.

When asking for consent, you will need to inform the patient in an easily understood way, of;

* The nature of the problem

* The treatment you propose

* The risks involved

* The benefits to be gained

* Expected outcomes

* What other alternatives may be available

After explaining, you must allow patients to ask questions, before they make a decision.

In most cases, consent for routine Chiropody is not really necessary, as the patient is implying consent by booking an appointment and arriving for it, however you should still make it clear what you intend to do. Where children are involved, you should take particular care in advising them and their parents or guardians of the treatment.

Expressed Consent is required when a procedure, such as nail surgery, or other treatments that may carry some risk, is to be performed. This will require written consent by signing a consent form. To reinforce the verbal information you have given to a patient about their treatment, it is advisable to back it up with written information.

A competent adult who has reached the age of 18 years and has the capacity to make decisions on behalf of their own treatment may give consent. Young people aged 16 and 17, who appear to have understood the treatment put to them, may give their own consent without separate parental consent. Children under the age of 16 may also give consent for themselves if you feel that they understand what is proposed and are competent enough to make their own decisions, although it is advised that a parent or guardian is involved in the decision making.

Confidentiality

To ensure records are kept confidential, you must ensure that they are stored in a lockable cabinet and unauthorized people are not allowed to view your patient's records. If you are keeping patient information on a computer, you will need to be registered with the Data Protection Registrar and ensure access is kept restricted to those members of staff whom it is relevant to.

Every day you will be told personal information by your patients. It may be about themselves, their medical history, their family or other people they know, as well as other sensitive information. As a Medical Professional, you have to treat all that a patient says to you as confidential, and your patients have a natural assumption that you will.

There may be times when you need to breach this confidentiality, by sharing information with a third party, for example a health care company. You may disclose medical history, diagnosis and treatment with them after seeking consent from the patient. By law you are required to report cases of abuse and domestic violence if a patient shares the information with you.

18 Minimum Clinical Standards

As well as trying to run a successful business, you also need to meet certain professional guidelines on minimum standards for your practice.

Your governing body should be able to issue you with their own guidelines or recommendations for minimum clinical standards.

Patient Care

You have an obligation to your patients to provide them with the greatest level of care you can and update and maintain your clinical skills through continuous development training.

Each patient must be treated as an individual and provided with all the information available regarding their treatment. Their records need to be clearly written, accurate and up to date, together with treatment plans and objectives. Records should be stored in a lockable cabinet. If you are using abbreviations on the patients' records it is advisable to keep a list of all the abbreviations you use. This makes it easier for other practitioners to understand your notes, but also, in a case of litigations, your notes will need to be discussed in a court of law.

As a professional, you should have good communication links with other health professionals who are involved in the care of your patients.

With certain patients, usually those under 16, you should ensure that another adult is present with you in the clinic room during treatment.

The clinic

The area you treat patients in should offer privacy and comfort. Your surgery needs to be equipped with sufficient lighting and ventilation, hand washing facilities, sterilisation equipment and waste collection facilities, as well as anything else you physically need to treat patients. Most of your electrical equipment will need to be safety tested every 1-2 years.

You should ensure a telephone is easily available to ring for assistance in an emergency.

Flammable drugs must be kept in a metal lockable cupboard, away from other drugs and dressings. Needles and syringes should also be stored in a lockable cupboard.

You should make sure that cross infection is kept to a minimum by having appropriate procedures in place, including;

* All instruments need to be sterilised to 134C–137C for a holding time of 3 minutes

* Ensure Sterilisers are regularly serviced and maintained

* Disposable gloves are worn during treatment

* Gloves are not to be worn for more than one patient

* Plastic Aprons should be used where there is a risk of fluids being splashed

* Sterile blades are for single use only

* All surfaces which come into contact with patients should be wiped clean using appropriate surface cleaning products

* Cuts or abrasions on your hands must be covered with a waterproof dressing

* All waste is disposed of appropriately.

When considering an autoclave, it is advisable to purchase a non vacuum steam steriliser for solid unwrapped instruments. A vacuum steriliser is required if you intend to sterilise wrapped instruments or those inside pouches. Steam sterilisers require a fresh supply of distilled water which does not contain contaminants. You can buy distilled water ready bottled from suppliers, or car maintenance stores which sell battery top up water. This is also distilled water. Another way of generating your own source of distilled water is to purchase a Water Distiller which purifies tap water ready for use in the autoclave.

It is recommended that a first aid box is kept on the premises and sufficient training in first aid and resuscitation is completed annually.

When performing nail surgery under a local anaesthetic, a minimum of one practitioner should be present. You will also need to attend a recognised course on basic life support.

Disposal of Clinical Waste

Because you are producing waste by treating patients, you will need to arrange for collection of the waste for incineration. All waste, including gloves, swabs, dressings, nail and hard skin cuttings etc. will need to be placed in yellow incineration waste bags. Sharps waste such as scalpels and needles need to be disposed of in a clearly marked yellow sharps bin which conforms to BS7320 and should never be more than three quarters full.

You cannot mix your clinical waste with your domestic rubbish. It is your responsibility to ensure that all your clinical waste is collected and disposed of appropriately.

When your waste is collected you should be issued with a clinical waste disposal certificate which may need to be produced to prove that you are acting responsibly.

Contact one of the companies listed in Appendix B to arrange collection of your waste or there may be a local company listed in the telephone directory which may be cheaper. Make sure they are registered with the Environmental Health Agency.

Disposal of clinical waste from a domiciliary visit

When you visit a patient in their own home, there are certain impracticalities in collecting waste.

If this is non infected waste, like the waste the patient would normally generate if they tended to their feet themselves, then it can be disposed in the patients own domestic waste. If infected waste is produced, which involves blood or other body fluids, you will need to make provisions to enable you to return the waste back to your clinic to be disposed of in the appropriate manner. All sharps need to be returned to the clinic for disposal.

Ideally you will require a water proof container to keep a yellow incinerator bag in, in the car. Any contaminated waste will need to be transferred to the yellow bag, then the container transferred to the clinic for disposal.

19 Public and Professional Indemnity and Liability

Now that you have set up a business you have certain legal responsibilities to the public, your employees and yourself. If someone is injured because of the treatment you have provided or negligence or lack of adequate health and safety measures, you are liable to be sued.

You will need to ensure you have adequate insurance cover to pay legal costs as well as any compensation, if you are found to be at fault.

Your professional indemnity insurance will be arranged through your governing body where as a separate premium through independent insurance companies will be needed for the others. Check with your governing body to see what is included in your yearly premiums, and what you will need in addition to provide adequate cover. Insurance is calculated on the estimated level of risk connected to your business, and what controls you have in place to reduce the risk of claims made against you.

Employers' Liability Insurance

This is an insurance you must have if you employ staff. If they are injured or suffer illness caused through working they can seek compensation from you. Your insurance must be for at least £5 Million, although most insurance companies will cover you up to £10 Million.

If you do not have appropriate insurance, the Health and Safety Executive, who enforce the law on Employers' Liability Insurance, can fine you up to £2,500 each day that you do not have appropriate insurance.

You can find an authorized Insurer by contacting the Association of British Insurers listed in Appendix B. Once you have insurance you will receive a certificate which must be displayed where employees can see it and keep copies for at least 40 years. The certificate will need to be shown when health and safety inspectors visit your premises.

If you are the only employee in the business you do not need Employers Liability Insurance. Family members who are employed in your business do not need cover either.

Public Liability Insurance

This covers any injury to members of the public as a result of them visiting your premises, or caused by you when you visit their home. It will pay out any compensation awarded as well as legal fees.

Product Liability Insurance

Any item which is sold or given to patients is classed as a product. Under the Consumer Protection Act 1987, you are legally responsible for any damage or injury caused by a product you supply, even though you did not manufacture the product. If you are supplying any products which could be harmful, you must ensure there are warning labels provided with the product.

Most Product Liability Insurance is between £0.5 Million and £5 Million, but check with your governing body as to what they may suggest as an appropriate level of cover.

Professional Indemnity Insurance

As a professional you will need to have adequate cover, incase a patient decides to pursue compensation as a result of treatment that you gave. Within your yearly subscription costs to your governing body, should be built in your Professional Indemnity Insurance. Check with them the level of insurance you have and add to it if necessary. It is advisable to be covered for £5 Million, unless you perform foot surgery, not nail surgery, where addition cover will be required.

To reduce the risk of claims, make sure that you have sufficient documentation and practice good record keeping.

20 Health and Safety

Because we are in a society of litigation, health and safety is more important now than it ever was. When patients are in your clinic, in the building or in your care, you are responsible for their well being. If you, your staff or members of the public come to harm, it can have serious consequences to your business in the short term as well as the long term.

The health and safety legislation was put into place to remove the risk to staff and the public, from accidents and hazards caused by the operation of the business.

If an accident has occurred, health and safety inspectors can enter and assess your premises and issue a legal notice stopping activity or requesting improvements. They can also prosecute a business or individual and you could be fined or even imprisoned.

You will need to inform the local authority of your intention to practice and to open the building to the public. They may send an inspector to look at the premises and suggest ways to minimize particular risks.

If you own or are responsible for the building you work from, you will need to carry out a risk assessment of potential hazards. If you are renting a room, make yourself aware of the health and safety measures the practice already has in place.

In order to show to the health and safety inspectors or local authority officers that you have addressed the potential hazards in the building, you will first need to identify them yourself. List all hazards, however trivial.

Once you have identified them you will need to assess the level of risk. It is classed as either a high or low risk of someone coming to harm by a potential hazard. What are the chances of patients or staff causing an injury to themselves from each of the hazards? You will then need to decide how you will reduce the level of risk of each one.

You must also make sure that there are adequate first aid facilities

Examples of potential hazards	
Chemicals	Repetitive tasks
Instruments	Seating
Desk heights	Slipping
Ceiling heights	Tripping
Lighting	Falling
Ventilation	Electricity cables / sockets
Manual handling	Stairs
High pressures in autoclaves	

in the building and appropriate training has been included for staff.

If you are using substances which are potentially dangerous, you will need to protect employees and others who may be at risk. Refer to the Control of Substances Hazardous to Health Regulations 2002 (COSHH) for more information. Any hazardous substance should be labelled appropriately and you should keep a safety information sheet about the chemical in the clinic. As part of your risk assessment you should ensure that employees follow the health and safety procedures you have in place to reduce any risk posed by hazardous subtstances. Appropriate and safe disposal of these substances will also need to be considered.

Make certain risks comply to the relevant legislation. Put all the risks and their control measures down on paper for others to read and

Examples of reducing risks	
Keep chemicals and instruments locked away	Fix loose cables away or under floors
Fit non slip flooring	Annual maintenance of equipment
Repair flooring so it is level	
Put up warning signs	Maintain an accident report book
Highlight edges of steps	
Fit stair rails	Ensure sufficient staff training

refer to. In addition, observe staff and patients in the practice and you may see potential risks you hadn't thought of. Don't forget to update your health and safety folder annually or when the need arises, if sooner.

You must also have procedures in place to report and record accidents that occur, as well as sufficient training for employees to make sure they are awaire of health and safety issues and the rules you have implemented.

Fire Safety

You and everyone who enters your premises, including patients, are responsible for contributing to the fire safety of the building. You will need to appoint yourself or another member of staff as a designated person who is responsible for the fire safety arrangements. If you rent part of the premises, then it is the owner of the building who is responsible. If you occupy the entire building then it is your responsibility.

As part of your risk assessment, you will have identified possible fire hazards, including;

* Machinery and Equipment

* Electricity, heating and lighting

* Flammable liquids

You will also need to look at areas which may be of great risk of allowing a fire to spread rapidly. How could you reduce the risk of fire or control it if it were to start? Maybe some of your doors should be replaced with toughened fire doors to help confine a fire. What additional control measures will you need to put into place?

You will need to ensure there are appropriate proceedures in place to

* Detect fires

* Fight Fires

* Evacuate the building

You should consider placing a fire detection system throughout the building, as well as appropriate extinguishers at strategic places. An emergency plan should be written up to include your evacuation procedure, collection point and information about contacting the fire brigade. A fire action notice should also be displayed in the practice to inform patients and staff of the evacuation procedure.

You should ensure that all fire extinguishers are tested and maintained regularly. Keep certificates of maintanence in a fire safety record book.

Escape routes should be indicated by clear signs and any electrical equipment regularly tested to reduce the risk of electrical faults occuring.

An inspection by the fire brigade will give you more specific advice on your building and how to minimize the risk of fire.

21 Marketing and Promotion

Once you have set up the clinic, you will need to invest in finding your patients. Without them, your business will soon run at a loss and fail. Patients will never know you are there unless they are told.

Advertising is an effective, but sometimes costly way of announcing your services, but there are certain ways to get free advertising and promotion for your practice. Communication with your patients is vital in order to retain existing patients, as well as gain new ones.

First appearances

You are the main representative of your business. If you look scruffy and untidy, what does it say about your business and the treatment patients may receive? How you look is very important. In a way it is part of your advertising and if you get it wrong it won't bring the patients into the clinic.

Contact some of the clothing companies in Appendix B for catalogues and choose a practical uniform or tunic which you think would make you look professional. Buy two or three sets of uniforms so that you can alternate them whilst you are washing others. If you go for a white uniform, make sure you wash it regularly otherwise it will soon show up the dirt.

Spend time in the morning getting to look respectable. Make sure you don't look as though you've just got out of bed with scruffy hair and stubble. It goes without saying that you should not be treating patients if you are under the influence of alcohol or drugs.

The appearance of your clinic is also on trial. It needs to be clean, tidy and professional. Paint the walls in a light colour and if possible hang paintings by local artists on the walls. This provides talking points for patients inside and outside the clinic, so they may tell their friends about you and the paintings, thereby providing free advertising for you. Talk to the artists and offer them wall space to sell their pictures and in return you get some nice pictures for your wall for free.

Apart from your clinic room, patients will be spending several minutes sat in the waiting or reception area, so why not try and make an impression there as well. Look at the comfort of the reception, firstly are the chairs comfortable? Is there an up to date selection of magazines to read? The reception area needs to be light and airy, but not too cold or too hot. Flowers and pictures around the room make the area inviting and visually interesting with background music to relax patients whilst they wait. Refreshments are always a pleasant addition to waiting rooms, whether it is a water supply or a fridge with soft drinks in. It is another talking point for patients to tell their friends.

Receptionists are your patients first contact with the practice. They should also look presentable, be efficient, but above all, pleasant to the patients. Patients are the priority, not paperwork and the receptionists focus should always be on the patients.

Advertising Media and Patient sources

Put yourself in the patient's shoes. If you've got a foot problem, where would you look to find your nearest Podiatrist? Make a list of all the places you can think of, together with the type of patient it would attract and think about how you can exploit that type of media to work to your advantage.

All of the advice in this section is based purely on the experiences and results that I have monitored through my own advertising. It may vary in different areas or locations, but you have got to remember to keep costs to a minimum and results to a maximum.

Telephone Directories
On the whole, Yellow Pages is the directory which most potential patients will look in to find their nearest Podiatrist. The circulation of Yellow Pages is huge and your advert has the potential to be inside each Yellow Pages in every local home. So, spending money here is well worth it. To spread the costs, you can enter an agreement with Yell (Yellow Pages) to pay in ten monthly interest free installments. What

you now have to do is design an advert which will stand out when listed against your competitors. You have to be the one they ring first.

As your business develops, it is often prudent to reduce the size of your advert and have a smaller one for people to refer to, when they are trying to find your telephone number and not select a new Podiatrist.

There are other telephone directories, which are worth having a listing in, but channeling most of your funding into the Yellow Pages is more cost effective.

Because the Yellow Pages are produced annually, there may be a period of time at the start when you won't have an advert in it, whilst waiting for the next edition. Contact Yell to discuss your advertising arrangements with a representative at least 6 months before the publication date. You won't start paying for the advert until the edition is released, but you need to allow a lot of preparation time for proofs of the advert to be approved or altered.

Local Newspapers

Advertising in a local newspaper can be a lottery. A good advert will yield potential patients, but it is a short lived advert, i.e. it is only in for the number of weeks you can afford. You are also relying on patients seeing your advert amongst all the others, from double glazing, blinds, cars etc., so it is not just other Podiatrists you will be in competition against here. Once again, if its going to be effective, its got to stand out.

Advertising in local newspapers can be expensive, but if this is the way you wish to advertise you need to spend the money to get some decent returns. Putting in a small advert in the middle of the paper saying who you are and your telephone number will yield very few, if any, results. A reasonable size advert which is duplicated in the same issue and repeated the following week will bring in plenty of results, but at a cost.

If you have a new business, or new development within the business, your local newspaper might be interested in making it into an article or feature. This is free, but back up the feature with an advert or promotional feature, such as money off their first visit. Contact the newspaper and tell them what you are doing, why it is newsworthy or relevant to their readers and how it can benefit the area and local people. If they agree to visit you and make a feature, they may also send a photographer, so get the clinic looking attractive, light, professional and well stocked. First impressions, as have already been mentioned, are very important.

Other Peoples' Appointment cards

Often local GP's or hospitals will offer you advertising space on their appointment cards or patient leaflets. This form of advertising will never cover the cost of your advert. Patients don't examine appointment cards except to transfer their appointment from the card onto their calendar. All it does is cover the printing costs of the cards or leaflets for the GP's or hospitals. It doesn't help you.

I have advertised on hospital appointment cards with a tried and tested successful advert, and on both occasions it has only yielded a couple of patients and proved to be a costly lesson in where to advertise.

If you want to advertise in a leaflet, get one of your own printed and leave that in GP practices or other clinics. Patients who are interested in Podiatry will pick one up if they want one.

Your Premises

Advertise in the premises you are working in. Put up a poster, leave leaflets, put up a name plaque outside, put up a sign on the door to the clinic, or in the window. Make the most of your premises. It is free and if there are patients coming in to see other professionals, they need to know you are there as well.

If your clinic is in a good location, passing trade should also notice the signs or plaque, thereby becoming informed of your services.

Leaflet Drops

Leaflet drops through letter boxes are a bit hit and miss. For this to be effective you will need to identify geographical areas which have a high proportion of your target audience, which is very difficult. Costs are pretty low, just the cost of photocopying and some leg work.

However, this form of advertising is quite unprofessional and you have to consider what type of image it is portraying to patients and other health professionals. I have never used this method of advertising.

Radio

Another media available for advertising is the radio. You will need to advertise locally, but consider what type of radio station your potential patients would listen to. They may not listen to a local modern station, but a national station devoted to classical music or an older style music. Would this be an effective use of your budget?

Other Health Professionals

Some of your patients will be referred from GP's or other Health Professionals, but how are they going to know about you?

Send a letter, together with a leaflet and business cards to GP's, Physiotherapists, Reflexologists, Osteopaths, Chiropractors or any other health professionals in the area. In the letter introduce yourself and explain the services you provide, include contact numbers and offer them the opportunity to allow you to visit them and talk about the clinic and its facilities. If they agree to your visit, take something with you like cakes or lunch. It realy does help them to remember you.

Talks and Presentations

Give free talks on Chiropody and Podiatry, Foot care, Foot wear or Injury prevention to relevant selective audiences.

Find your local Women's Institute Groups, Arthritis Groups, Diabetic Groups, Age Concern or Retirement Centres and offer to talk to them about a subject relevant to them and promotional for you. Don't forget to take lots of leaflets and business cards with you. To really encourage new patients into your clinic, you could even take some vouchers for discounted treatment. Make your presentation professional, informative and relaxed. Don't talk down to people, encourage them to approach you and ask questions and take things for them to look at or touch and examine.

Talks are a great way to address a large number of potential patients who are all within your criteria for people who could use your clinic. Look in your local newspaper. There will probably be a section on groups or organizations who meet in the local area. Select which would be potential patients and what sort of talk would be of interest to them. All it costs is a bit of time, effort and printing.

Free Promotion

Any free services you can provide will give you valuable promotion.

Provide free Podiatry at local marathons for the runners at the finish line. It will take some of your time and some supplies, but if you tell the local newspapers what you are doing they may do an article on you.

Volunteer to provide Podiatry for the homeless at Christmas at a local homeless shelter. This service is greatly appreciated by the patients and again provides valuable promotion for you from newspapers or even radio coverage.

If you wish to take your practice along the Biomechanical route, offer a free Podiatry Advice Service to your local sports centre or athletics club. If they need treatment then refer them into your clinic.

Designing an effective advert

Advertising is a waste of time and money if the advert does not catch anyone's attention and get them into the clinic. There are a few simple guidelines to get your advert noticed, and you don't need to spend a huge amount of money to achieve it. If you go for a really big advert, it doesn't mean you will get a lot more responses. Don't forget we are trying to attract the attention of people who are only intending to spend around £17 for a treatment, not thousands of pounds on a new car or conservatory. You don't need a big advert. Most of the adverts I have used in the past have been about 10 cm long by about 7 cm wide and on average each has resulted in about 28 new patients coming to the clinic. Treat your patients right and that 28 become recurring patients and so do another 28 of their friends. The growth of your practice therefore develops exponentially, i.e. 1 tells 2, 2 tell 4, 4 tell 8, 8 tell 16, 16 tell 32 etc., but to get this growth your initial advert needs to be impressive.

With all your advertising, keep a copy of the advert you use, where it goes and how much it costs. Then, when the patients start to come in and you find out that they responded to certain adverts, you can keep a tally of which adverts have been effective and which haven't. If they are being printed in a newspaper, buy a copy of the issue they are printed in and see if you can find the advert yourself. Chances are, if you are scanning quickly through it, you might miss it. If you do, how effective is it going to be with people who aren't actually looking for it?

Guidelines for adverts	
Big is not beautiful	Offer them a bargain
Grab their attention	Tell them what they need to do
Don't waffle	Duplicate the advert
Be clear and concise	Monitor all results

The first thing you need to consider is the headline. This is the first line of text which people see. Most people will scan through the newspaper, so if your headline is not eye-catching or large enough, they will scan right past it, even if they are particularly looking for a Podiatrist.

Bob Supermax is at 12 Corn Lane, Nailstone, Scalpelshire. Telephone (01234) 567890 for an appointment today, for all your Podiatry needs	**Chiropody** 12 Corn Lane, Nailstone, Scalpelshire. Telephone **(01234) 567890** for an appointment

The example on the left announces an advert from Bob Supermax, but if the potential patients haven't been to you before, how will they know who you are? They are more likely to skip the advert because you only find out at the bottom of the advert what it is Bob provides.

The second advert is instantly more eye catching and informative. The first line tells the potential patient that it is an advert about Chiropody (which is more likely to get a response to the less used term Podiatry), the second line tells the patient where it is provided and the third line tells them how to make an appointment.

Other headlines that work well include:

Painful Feet? Call **(01234) 567890** to see a **Chiropodist** 12 Corn Lane, Nailstone, Scalpelshire.	**Feet Hurt?** Contact the **Chiropodist** at 12 Corn Lane, Nailstone, Scalpelshire. Telephone **(01234) 567890** for an appointment

In these examples the headline is what the patients may be experiencing and the solution (the word Chiropodist) is also highlighted and larger than the surrounding text.

Most of the examples already shown contain very few words. When scanning a newspaper, people do not have the time to read every word in an advert. They pick out the words which are relevant to them, so don't fill up all of your advert space with text. Blank areas in the newspaper are almost as noticeable as colour pictures. Keep your advert simple, tell them what you are offering, and how to get it and nothing more. An advert is not an efficient use of space if you try and educate patients on what they should be doing about their corns or verrucaes. Your aim is to get them into the clinic. The following advert might have the right headline, be informative and polite, but very few people will have kept their attention long enough to get to the end of the advert.

Chiropody

is available from the Podiatry clinic in Corn Lane with Bob Supermax. The clinic is modern and comfortable and equipped with the latest technology. Bob offers a range of treatments to help with all kinds of foot problems and would be more than delighted to see you in the clinic or in the comfort of your own home if that were more convenient. If you would like to contact the receptionist to make an appointment then please telephone (01234) 567890.

Another way to get instant reaction to an advert is to offer potential patients money off their first treatment. I found that offering a discount of £5 if they brought the advert with them at the time of the appointment, yielded twice as many new patients than just offering them a free tube of cream. As well as the headline and contact details being prominent and eye catching, the fact that you are offering a discount will also need to be noticeable. Some people notice the monetary discount before they read the headline and may only come and see you because they will be getting something cheaper than they would otherwise, and may not actually have a foot problem. On the advert you will also need to make it clear when the offer runs out, otherwise patients may cut out the advert, but never actually get round to telephoning and making an appointment. By giving them a time limit, it encourages a quicker and greater response. I would suggest a 6 weeks maximum date limit, although 4 weeks is more normal.

Feet Hurt?
Telephone
(01234) 567890 for a
Chiropody appointment

Save £5 off your first
treatment on presentation of
this advert.
Only one offer per person
Valid until 31 December 2005

12 Corn Lane, Nailstone,
Scalpelshire.

Chiropody

12 Corn Lane,
Nailstone,
Scalpelshire.

Telephone
(01234) 567890
for an appointment

Save £5
off your first treatment.
Valid until 31 December 2005
Only one offer per person

Consider putting a picture in the advert, but not at the expense of it being too cluttered. Keep the picture relevant to what you are offering. Don't put a picture of the clinic, people won't know what it is. I found that putting in a faded drawing of a foot behind the text with the headline 'Chiropody' got quite a lot of attention. Using a colour photograph will add expense to your advert, and for it to be clear enough, the advert will probably need to be bigger than you intend (see page 120 for an example).

I have used the advert on page 120 on numerous occasions with some good results. Repeating the advert in the same edition as well as the following weeks edition gives greater coverage and patients are more likely to notice you.

Go through a local newspaper and look through the small adverts.

Chiropody

Save £5.00

off your first treatment, on
presentation of this advert

Offer only valid until
31 December 2005
Only one offer per person

12 Corn Lane,
Nailstone, Scalpelshire

Telephone
(01234) 567890
to make an appointment

Which ones catch your eye? Which ones stand out as soon as you turn the page? Look at what others are doing because your advert will be in competition with them for viewers attention, regardless of what they are advertising.

When advertising in the Yellow Pages, your advert needs to be a little bit more factual, but again it needs to stand out against the other Podiatry adverts. Patients have made a conscious decision to find a Podiatrist, so have already turned to the relevant page and somehow your advert has got to impress them more than the others. Your headline needs to be different from a newspaper advert. There needs to be more information to help patients to choose a more comprehensive and professional practice.

I used a similar advert to the following one, but with a colour photograph instead of the black and white footprint, in the Yellow Pages for one year. It was so successful, I decided not to run it the second year, because I didn't have the capacity in my clinic to cope with the extra number of patients it was generating. This was great for the business in two ways. I got a lot of new patients and the business running to full capacity, and after the first year, I saved on my advertising budget because I didn't need it so much. Existing patients will always need to refer to your listing in Yellow Pages, so that they can find your number if they've lost it, so always keep an entry in the directory, but if you can afford to reduce the size, without making your business suffer, your business will be financially better off.

Bob Supermax

Chiropodist / Podiatrist

- Routine Chiropody - Nail Care, Corns, Callus and Verrucae
- Ingrowing Toenails and Nail Surgery
- Insoles and Orthotics
- Specialist in Sports Injuries, Arthritis and Children
- Home Visits also available

(01234) 567890
12 Corn Lane, Nailstone, Scalpelshire

Encouraging Word of Mouth

How can you encourage patients to recommend you to their friends? You can't make patients talk about you, can you? Yes you can. This sounds too good to be true, but all businesses have the capacity to advertise for very little, by encouraging word of mouth and introducing patient's friends to your service. Patients who are referred to you via word of mouth are also more likely to become loyal repetitive customers. If your existing patients recommend you to their friends, you are getting new patients at very little cost, in comparison to newspaper advertising.

Patients are likely to recommend you if you provide them with a good, professional and competent treatment, but only if asked. What you have to do is find ways of encouraging the existing patients to talk about you unprompted.

Give something away

One way is to exceed their expectations and give good value for money. If you provide more than they expect, they are more likely to spontaneously tell their friends.

Example 1

Mrs Brown, 'I was at Bob Supermax's Podiatry clinic the other day and when he finished he gave me a tube of cream to try for free!'
Mrs Owen, 'Oh that's good. I wouldn't mind some cream myself, I think I'll get my feet done there as well then.'

In this example, Mrs Brown didn't expect she would receive a free tube of cream, and as such it acted as a prompt to tell her friend, Mrs Owen, about the clinic.

Giving something away can help your clinic in 3 ways. First, it helps to maintain loyalty from the existing patient. Second, it encourages the patient to talk about you thereby introducing their friends to you and third, you are introducing a product, such as a cream, which can then be purchased by the patient from you in the future. Although you may feel that you are giving away your profit, you will gain it back many times over in other forms. You could use this type of promotion at certain times of the year, e.g. Christmas or your Anniversary of opening, in the guise of a celebratory gift.

Example 2

Another way of giving something away and encouraging word of mouth is to contact the patient after a treatment with a letter and voucher. In the letter write about the service they received, prompting the patient about certain aspects of the service and encouraging the patient to recommend you to their friends. The letter should be sent out within a week after their appointment. Target new patients, or if you are having a quiet period, all patients who come in within a month. Make a note in the patient's record that you have sent them a letter and voucher, as it saves you looking blank when they come back in and thank you for the voucher. Make the voucher date sensitive, i.e., give them a limited, but reasonable time to use the voucher. This will act as a prompt for them to come back to you. The original first treatment has now produced at least two more treatments; the existing patient's follow up treatment, as well as her friend's she talks to about the voucher.

An example of a typical letter is given below. Design a separate voucher to go in with the letter, which includes your name, address, telephone number, Expiry date and voucher value.

Bob Supermax
B.Sc. (Hons) Pod MChS SRCh
Podiatrist

12 Corn Lane,
Nailstone,
Scalpelshire SC1 1NS
(01234) 567890

Dear Mrs Brown,

You recently visited the Podiatry clinic in Corn Lane, I hope you were pleased with the service you received there.

As a way of thanking you for using the service, I would like to present you with a voucher for £5 which you can use in part payment for treatment at the clinic at your next visit.

If you were happy with the treatment you received, the promptness of service or the professionalism of the clinician, then please recommend us to your friends.

I look forward to seeing you at your next visit,

Yours sincerely

Bob Supermax

This type of letter could also be sent to patients who haven't been for a few months and need reminding of your service, or if you have developed new services within the business as an advert to patients.

Example 3

If you are going to give something away which is relevant to your business, useful to your patients and which encourages repeated use of your clinic and word of mouth recommendation, think about what products would be relevant. Giving a key ring or pen away with you name and phone number on, are not really items you associate with Podiatry clinics. Foot creams, Files and other foot health items are more applicable. Why not consider putting your name and phone number on the handle of a large emery board or long handled shoe horn, an item which patients will use regularly and associate with you. Patients normally would buy these from you, but to make effective word of mouth give them away free as they are relatively inexpensive. This type of promotion can also be done by producing your own brand of foot cream, although this would prove to be more expensive.

To produce these personalized items, have a look in your local telephone directory under Promotional Gifts and Incentives, and discuss your requirements with them.

Be Unique

There's not going to be a huge amount of difference between you and your competitors, so you have to appear to be different in your approach, treatment or handling of your business.

Example I

Because patients are sitting in your waiting room whilst they wait for their appointment time, why not try a unique approach to comfort and surroundings. You could provide a drinks machine for patients use, but is that new or different? Why not put a bowl of fruit in the waiting area for patients to eat. It is unique, promotes a health conscious image and encourages patients to talk about you. To encourage patients to eat the fruit you will need to have a sign next to the bowl, otherwise they may be too polite and not realize it is for themselves to eat.

> Please help yourself to this complimentary fruit and tell others about the unique approach to health you receive at the Bob Supermax Podiatry Clinic.

Example 2

Putting a vase of flowers in the waiting area looks attractive, but doesn't really inspire conversation, unless it is an unusual bouquet of exotic flowers. A striking display of flowers more inspiring than carnations or roses will generate a reaction. Put them in the window of the reception area for even greater impact, so pedestrians will notice them. Your name and clinic will then be linked to the flowers, so when your patients comment on the flowers they saw to their friends, your name will inevitably come up. Don't put a sign up saying that the flowers were supplied by the flower shop, otherwise the word of mouth advertising you generate will become directed at the flower shop and not at you.

Example 3

Magazines in the waiting room need to be up to date and renewed on a regular basis. Patients like to read something whilst waiting and if it's two years out of date it is uninspiring. New magazines are a novelty in waiting areas. Patients read or see something in the magazine which is newsworthy to them and pass on this piece of news to their friends. They will also pass on the information about what magazine they read it in and where the magazine was, i.e. your clinic.

To make this a doubly effective advertising tool, why not remove all old magazines after 1-2 months and donate them to a local hospital, Age Concern or Retirement centre. Before you take the magazines to them, put a sticker on the front of the magazines saying where they were donated from, together with a telephone number.

> This magazine was kindly donated for
> your reading pleasure by
>
> **The Bob Supermax**
> **Podiatry Clinic,**
> 12 Corn Lane, Nailstone.
> *Telephone (01234) 567890*
> *for an appointment*

Encourage clarity of thought

Patients are not always very good at putting their thoughts into words, and if they are going to explain to their friends how good you are, what the standard of care is like or why they should also go to you, it is sometimes better if you can encourage them to think about what they would say before they say it.

Example

Provide a feedback form for patients to fill in after they have had treatment. It could be handed to them when they leave or sent to them in the post, either way, you are encouraging them to think about the service you have provided. You will need to consider carefully what questions you are going to ask in order to get the correct stimulus.

* Did you enjoy the treatment you received?

* Was the Podiatrist Informative?

These types of questions really only requires a Yes or No answer and don't get the patient thinking about their experience. Try the questions below, they encourage more thought and the formation of at least a sentence in response.

* If we could have done one thing differently for you today, what would it have been?

* What three things would you consider to be the most important when it comes to providing you with a Podiatry service?

* How does the service we provide compare to others you may have experienced?

As well as helping the patients to formulate and evaluate an impression of the service they have received, it is also providing you with valuable feedback to help improve your service or identify areas which need to be reassessed.

First Year's Advertising Campaign

Because your budget is limited, you will need to invest it wisely. The following table is an example of one year's possible advertising campaign and how it could help to increase your business, as well as generate profits.

The number of new patients each media generates is highlighted in the months in which it was used.

	J	F	M	A	M	J	J	A	S	O	N	D	Total
Newspaper Article	10												10
Newspaper Advert	20	20	20			20							80
Talks	10			10			10						30
Clinic Advertising		2	2	2	2	2	3	3	3	3	3	3	28
Recommendation				2	3	3	3	4	4	5	5	6	35
Direct Referrals					1	1	2	2	2	3	3	3	17
Yellow Pages							12	12	12	12	12	12	72

Newspaper Article (Free)
Invite the local newspaper to the clinic to do a promotional feature on you and the services you provide when your clinic opens. This is free and should start the ball rolling in bringing new patients into the clinic.

Newspaper Advert (£250 each time)
Yes, it seems to cost a lot, but you've got to let the patients know you are there. Have the same advert repeated in a single issue then repeat it once a month for the first three months, then again in June. Don't forget to make your advert date sensitive if encouraging them with a voucher.

Talks (Free)
Contact local groups who may be interested in having you as a speaker. I have only included three talks at three month intervals, but if you can

get more, then go for it. Don't forget that you will have a certain amount of free time at the start of your business venture, so you may as well use it productively in promoting the clinic.

Clinic Advertising (Free)
Put up your posters and leave the leaflets around and you will slowly generate some interest from patients who may already use the other facilities within your practice. Don't forget to put a name plaque outside to catch the attention of passing potential patients.

Recommendation (Free)
This type of patient referral can be slow, but look at the ideas in the previous section on generating word of mouth. Recommendation of patients will soon become your biggest source of referrals, and your cheapest.

Direct Referrals (Free)
Slowly, other professionals will become aware of the service you provide and have more confidence in using you. Get on good terms with other health professionals as communication with them is as important as that with patients.

Yellow Pages (£1,000 campaign)
As you will probably not be able to start your yellow pages advertising until the next edition, which may be some months after you start practicing, I have suggested a campaign of advertising in Yellow Pages which, in my example, starts in July and will continue until June the following year. You should receive a steady stream of new patients from advertising in the Yellow Pages.

First Year's Total Advertising Budget
As you can see, a lot of the ways to get people into your clinic can be at a very low cost or actually free. The cost of advertising for this first year totals £2,000 and is entirely spent on printed adverts in the newspaper and Yellow Pages. Your £2,000 has converted into 655 patient contacts for the first year. Don't forget that the year's advertising you have already paid for in the Yellow Pages will also keep running for another 6 months after the end of this one year.

If you can get interest free payments on your Yellow Pages Advert, you can make your first year's advertising budget even smaller. It would then work out at only £1,500 for this one years advertising from January to December.

The more effort you can put in at the start will not only bring immediate results, but also long term financial stability. Take every opportunity to promote yourself and the clinic.

22 Communicating with Patients

You've spent all this money telling everyone that you are open for business, promoting yourself to other professionals and groups and creating an appealing and friendly environment for your patients, but you also need to work hard on retaining them and encouraging them to return; otherwise you will have to advertise continually to replace the ones you are losing.

Patients are not only paying for a Podiatry service, they are paying for a level of care and attention that they haven't received elsewhere. This includes the promptness or efficiency of your service, your expert treatment and the pleasant and friendly staff.

We have already looked at innovative ways to encourage patients to come back, by encouraging them with letters and vouchers, so make it part of your yearly schedule to spend time going through existing patient records, sorting out the ones who haven't been for six months, and writing to them. This is much cheaper than re advertising and could also help generate word of mouth recommendation.

But what about the patients that come into the clinic? How can you increase patient loyalty? The way you communicate with them is vital. It should go without saying that you need to be polite and pleasant at all times and provide the respect you would expect to receive from others if it were you receiving the treatment.

In America, for all types of services there is generally more of a 'tipping' culture than we have in Britain, and the level of service you receive because of the anticipation of a tip, can be a lot higher. If you need motivation, imagine your fee is the tip, so be exceptionally nice to each patient, even if you feel lousy. By doing more than the patient expects, you are more likely to retain them as a loyal patient.

Make patients feel like part of your family. By this, I don't mean take them home for dinner, but if they look on you as a friend, they will look forward to coming to visit you and you can look forward to a regular fee. Talk to patients about their life, home, family, holidays etc. without being too intrusive. In turn they will gradually get to know certain aspects of your life too. Sharing information is a great way of promoting a friendly, caring and trusting relationship. Make notes in the patient's record of what you talked about and look in the record at their next visit to remind you to ask certain things.

Example

You made a note in Mrs Brown's record that her daughter was getting married and going to Jamaica for the honeymoon. When Mrs Brown returns and you ask her how the wedding went and if her daughter enjoyed Jamaica, she will be very impressed, thinking it was your memory and interest in her that made you ask. This is good promotion and helps develop profitable patient relationships.

For your sake however, you will need to know where the boundaries are. There will be certain patients with whom you won't feel comfortable sharing much information about yourself, as well as other patients who won't want to share information about themselves with you. Be careful with what you say to some patients, use your judgment and skills at reading non verbal cues to judge how to approach and talk to each patient. Gradually, as you see your patient's time and again, you will develop a practitioner-patient relationship. Don't take this relationship any further than the 30 minutes that they are with you in the clinic. Don't socialise with patients or accept invitations from them and don't give away your home address or phone number. This may seem a bit harsh, but there are some odd people in the world. Above all you are a professional, so act in a professional but friendly and caring way.

Try to avoid talking about 'touchy' subjects like politics and religion. You may not agree with the patients' views, but disagreeing with them and arguing your point will only lose you patients. Even if you don't agree with them, try being diplomatic when responding to their views, or keep your opinion to yourself.

Patients also respond well to education. Take time and effort to explain to them about the foot problems they are experiencing, what causes them, how best to treat them as well as what the patients can do themselves at home. By providing them with the knowledge of their problem, it helps to justify your role as a competent and qualified practitioner. If a friend of the patients asks her how her feet are, she can better inform her friend at the same time as giving you a glowing recommendation.

A good form of education which works well to encourage word of mouth promotion for your practice, is having some information leaflets printed. You may find that you repeat a lot of information when giving patients advice, so why not put it in the form of an A5 leaflet, printed from your computer, ready to hand out to patients when required. Don't forget to put your name, address and phone number somewhere on the leaflet for the patients to refer to, or the patient's friends to refer to if the leaflet gets passed on.

Find out via anonymous questionnaires, or verbal feedback what your patients like or dislike about your service and make it an immediate priority to change anything negative. This may range from delays in answering the telephone to availability of appointments. By showing that you are listening to the patients' opinions makes them feel valued and that they have in some way contributed to the development of the practice.

23 Dealing with Complaints

Negative advertising can be detrimental to your business, so deal with it immediately. If a patient rings up complaining that their toe has been hurting since their last visit, then ask them to come back to the clinic as soon as possible so you can have another look at it. If this means sacrificing your tea break or lunch break, so be it. When they come in treat them and reassure them, and don't charge them. Do this even if the problem could have been caused after the patient left the clinic. They will still associate the problem with their visit, and therefore always associate a bad toe with you, which is what they will tell their friends. People are always more likely to talk about things that went wrong or don't meet with their approval, more than things that are good.

When dealing with complaints there are certain ways of handling patients.

Dealing with complaints
* Let the patient talk about the problem without interruptions
* Be sympathetic and understanding of the problem
* Show interest by asking questions after they have talked about the problem
* Provide alternative reasons for the problem other than you or your treatment
* If further treatment is required give it to them free of charge
* Contact the patient a few days later to see if the problem has resolved

Don't tell patients that they are wrong in their reasoning about their problem. This leads to confrontation and patients leaving with a negative image of your business. If they leave feeling angry, they are likely to tell the first person they meet, what they are angry about and this is bad publicity for you.

The most amount of complaints you are likely to receive will be from patients who are disgruntled at having to pay for non attendance. You will have to decide whether or not you are going to charge for non attendance and what effect it may have on your business if you don't.

24 Managing your Waste

Under the Conrtolled Waste Regulation 1992, you must ensure appropriate and safe disposal of all clinic waste generated by your business. This waste must be collected seperately from domestic waste, and must be stored in yellow incineration waste bags. A separate bag must be used for each day and must be filled upto a maximum of three quarters full.

Clinical waste includes,

* Human tissue, including blood, even if it is not infected

* Swabs and dressings contaminated with human tissue or fluids

* Other soiled waste from treatment areas

You will need to arrange for collection of the waste for incineration. When your waste is collected you should be issued with a clinical waste disposal certificate which may need to be produced to prove you are acting responsibly.

Contact one of the companies listed in Appendix B to arrange collection of your waste or there may be a local company listed in the telephone directory which may be cheaper. Make sure they are registered with the Environmental Health Agency.

Collection of sharps

Syringe needles, cartridges and contaminated scalpels will need to be placed in a sharps container which should be sealed when three quarters full and disposed of through your clinical waste collector. Sharps bins must not be put inside a yellow incinerator bag, but left separate, labelled and once sealed not reopened. The containers themselves must conform to BS7320.

Disposal of clinical waste from a domiciliary visit

When on a domiciliary visit you will generate some waste. If this is non infected waste, like the waste the patient would normally generate if they tended to their feet themselves, then it can be disposed in the patients domestic waste. If infected waste is produced, which involves blood or other body fluids, you will need to make provisions to enable you to return the waste back to the clinic to be disposed of properly.

Ideally you will require a water proof container to keep a yellow incinerator bag in, in the car. Any contaminated waste will need to be transferred to the yellow bag, then the container transferred to the clinic for disposal.

All sharps will need to be returned to the clinic for safe disposal as well. When in a patients home remove blades from scalpel handles and place within a small sharps container held inside the domiciliary bag. When that is three quarters full it should then be placed inside the larger sharps box held within the clinic for disposal in the normal manner.

25 Accounting and Book Keeping

Running a successful Podiatry practice does, unfortunately, mean that there will be a certain amount of book keeping to do. This all revolves around the financial side of the business. Only a basic level of mathematical skill is required, but if you can efficiently monitor your cash flow, payments and expenses, you will find that running the business is much more organised and hassle free. It can also save you money as your Accountant, who will calculate your Tax and National Insurance payments, will charge you less if there is less work for him to do in organising your finances.

Keeping records is also a legal requirement. Because you are self employed you will need to keep your records for a minimum of five years and ten months after the end of that tax year.

Running a Monthly Account

The easiest way to keep a close eye on the finances of the business is to keep a monthly account. Don't let the receipts, invoices, cheque stubs etc. mount up until the end of your financial year. (Your financial year runs from the month you start trading to the following year. This may be different from the Inland Revenues Tax year which runs from the 6th April to the 5th April the following year.)

Every month, keep a tally of the patients you treat and what they paid you. An example of a useful income sheet is included in Appendix C. It may also be a good idea to keep a note of the form of payment they give you, whether cash, cheque or credit card. Pay the cash and cheques into your bank account on a regular basis to avoid keeping large sums of money on the premises. At the end of the month add up all your receipts (money paid to you) and enter it in your ledger book. You now need to list all the payments (money paid by you) that occurred in the month. Include all your business expenses, including:

1. **Payments to Creditors**

   A payment to creditors is the term used for other businesses who send you an invoice, or to which you make payment. These are the companies who provide your supplies, Insoles, stationery etc. Invoices often have up to 30 days in which they need to be paid, so make the most of it. Money is better kept in your account than in someone else's, but make sure you don't take too long paying your invoices as additional charges may then apply.

2. **Equipment / Machinery**

   List these separately to your other expenses. Your Accountant will need to know this so that he can calculate the yearly depreciation of the equipment, which is then taken into account when he calculates your annual Tax payment.

3. **Rent / Lease / Mortgage**

4. **Utilities**

   Enter all payments concerned with the building you are renting or leasing or the mortgage repayment, as well as the utility costs including gas, electricity, water and business rates.

5. **Telephone**

   Include the cost of telephones, mobile phones and the Internet used in the running of the business.

6. **Staff Wages**

   If you are employing staff, you will need to include their wages, National Insurance and Tax Payments, together with any Pension contributions you have made on their behalf.

7. **Drawings**

   Your salary is known as 'Drawings.' This is the amount of money which you are taking directly from the business as your salary for running it. This you can take in several different forms, either as a percentage of the gross profit (before deductions), or the net profit (after deductions) or as a fixed amount every month. However you decide to take it, you must be sure it is enough to cover your personal expenses (as calculated in the Business Plan) but not too much to drain the business of its cash flow.

8. **Pension**

It is a good idea to contribute into a pension as soon as possible in preparation for retirement. Your business will be an asset to sell at retirement. However, a pension can provide you with an initial lump sum, together with an annual income when it matures.

You can set up a pension through your business bank, which should have low costs for setting it up and managing it. Monthly payments are paid into your pension fund, which accumulates until you decide to retire. It is then used to provide you with an income. Some of it may be taken as a tax free lump sum.

As a self employed contributor to your pension, you can claim tax relief on your pension contributions in your annual accounts. This means that when calculating your annual tax liability, a percentage of your pension contributions will be deducted from your tax bill. You will be able to start taking your pension from the age of 60 and the value will be dependent on the amount invested over the years, the profit from investing and the charges it has occurred. Your pension contributions are invested by the company managing it, based on your preferences and their advice. It is usually invested in the financial markets either at home or abroad.

The contributions you pay towards your pension plan will need to be included for your annual tax return.

Seek independent financial advice on which pension is the most suitable for you.

9. **Savings** (For Tax payments or expansion)

Save regularly so that when your tax bill comes there will be money ready to pay it and it won't be such a shock. Put your savings into an account which pays interest on it. Your accountant will need to know how much interest is paid on all your bank accounts, including your own personal ones, to include in your tax return.

Sole traders pay income tax on the profit that the business makes, whereas Partnerships pay tax on their share of the profit when it has been divided between each individual partner.

10. **Vehicle Expenses**

You will need to keep a tally on the number of miles you travel for the business and provide this for your Accountant. The mileage form in Appendix C should be completed daily in order to keep on top of it, and added up at the end of each month.

You can purchase a vehicle through your business, but it will affect your tax payments. Another way to fund a vehicle is to lease hire it. This is when you pay a monthly charge to a lease hire firm and, in return, they provide you with a vehicle and pay for servicing, MOTs and Road Fund Licence. This can work out to be much more effective in maintaining your cash flow. Other vehicle expenses you need to include are Insurance and Petrol costs.

11. **Bad Debts**

Every now and then you may receive a patient's cheque back from their bank without being paid. If this is the case, it is classed as a bad debt. Go back to the patient who originally gave it to you and explain what happened and ask for either another cheque or better still, the cash and include the fee the bank has charged you for returning it. Because we deal with small amounts of money it can be too expensive trying to recover bad debts if you are having trouble contacting the patient for repayment. Make a note of it on the patient's record, inform the receptionist, and don't allow the person concerned to book another appointment until all their debts are paid.

12. **Training**

Training expenses can be put through your business. It is for the benefit of the business that you are doing further training, so it should pay for the travel costs getting there, the accommodation whilst there and the cost of the course.

13. **Insurance**
Include any insurances relating to the business. This may be Employers' Liability Insurance, Insurance for the contents or building you work in or Professional Indemnity Insurance.

14. **Professional Fees**
The Professional Fees you have to pay every year will need to be included. These fees include all memberships to professional bodies, and those which entitle you to retain your professional qualification or title.

15. **Accountants Fees**

16. **Maintenance Fees**
Fees paid to professionals who help with the running of the business, such as Maintenance engineers or servicing contracts you have for your autoclave, can be included in your expenses list.

17. **Advertising**
Advertising costs need to be included. It is good for you to see how your costs vary over the years, whilst still maintaining a healthy and successful business.

Subtracting the total expenses from the total of receipts you received each month will give you a running total of what your business bank balance is.

Accountants and Tax Returns

Every year, take a box file with all the information relating to that years business to your Accountant. Include a copy of the monthly accounts you did in your ledger book, together with bank statements and copies of your own personal bank accounts, which show interest payments, and any other documents showing other income or tax payments if you are working part time.

Your Accountant will then prepare your tax return. This is the form you will need to sign, which will then be sent to the Inland Revenue. Once it has been confirmed, your Accountant will tell you what you need to pay to the Inland Revenue and when. Tax payments are usually made twice a year. The first payment is the amount of tax due, in addition to half again towards your following year's tax bill, and this is due at the end of January. The second payment is the other half towards next years tax bill, and is due at the end of July.

Example

Your Accountant says that your tax bill is £3,000. In January you will need to pay the £3,000 plus £1,500 towards next year's bill. Total payable in January would be £4,500. In July the second half towards next year is required, i.e. the other £1,500, so this will need to be paid then. By next year, you will have already paid £3,000 towards that year's tax bill.

Tax is effectively paid a year in arrears, but start saving a little straight away so that you are prepared for your first tax payment.

Example

If you start trading in April 2005, your first year's tax year won't finish until March 2006. You then submit your tax returns and your first payments will then be due January 2007 and July 2007.

Included in your tax returns will be your contributions to National Insurance. This goes towards our state pension, unemployment benefits as well as many other benefits. There are different types of National Insurance to pay at different rates, and are all linked to earnings. Most self employed people will pay Class 2 and Class 4 contributions.

Class 2 Contributions are calculated on a weekly flat rate fee (currently £2.10 a week) and paid to HM Revenue and Customs quarterly or by direct debit.

Class 4 contributions are paid in addition to Class 2, by people whose business earns over a certain limit during the tax year. You must pay 8 per cent on profits between £4,985 and £32,760 plus 1 per cent on any profit over that amount.

If you decide to organise your own tax returns, you will need to contact your local Inland Revenue office for all the relevant forms and information. There are deadlines for tax returns and stiff financial penalties if you don't meet them.

Sometimes the Inland Revenue may make enquiries into your tax return and contact you explaining their intentions. This is not necessarily because they suspect you of providing false returns, but routine sampling of businesses. You should co-operate and provide them with the information they require, or your Accountant can deal with it on your behalf.

26 Registering for VAT

When a business buys goods it pays VAT on that purchase. When it sells goods or a service it charges VAT on those sales. If a business receives more VAT from sales than it pays for goods, the difference needs to be paid to HM Revenue and Customs. If a business has received less VAT on its sales than it has paid on goods, it will receive a refund from HM Revenue and Customs.

Most businesses have to register for VAT once their annual turnover exceeds £60,000; however Chiropody and Podiatry is exempt from VAT and you are not required to register. You will still have to pay the VAT on goods sold to you though.

27 Continual Professional Development

As part of your professional development you should be embarking on a continual programme of education every year. This is to ensure standards and safety are kept at a high level. Because the titles 'Chiropodist' and 'Podiatrist' are now protected, the Health Professions Council requires Continual Professional Development (CPD) of its members in order for you to retain your title. You must maintain an accurate and up to date record of any CPD activity, demonstrate that the CPD activity that you have done is relevant to your current or future practice, and present a portfolio proving you have maintained sufficient CPD activities for that period.

CPD activities can include;

* Work based learning. Including learning by physically doing the work, case studies, discussions with colleagues, in service training.

* Professional activity. Being a member of a professional body, Teaching.

* Formal Education. Attending courses, undertaking research, further education, attendance at conferences.

* Self Directed Learning. Reading Journals and articles, reviewing books and articles.

If requested you must provide evidence of any of the activities listed above, to demonstrate that sufficient development has been completed for that year.

When you are self employed, you are responsible for managing and maintaining your CPD activity. If you attend courses, you will be able to include the cost of the course in your business expenses, as well as the accommodation and travelling expenses involved in attending that course. The annual fees of the Health Professions Council can also be included in your business expenses, so don't forget to include them when you submit your accounts to your Accountant or HM Revenue and Customs.

To find a course which would develop your professional skills or further develop the practice, look in your journal, there may even be free up date courses available on line listed there.

28 Taking time off

You are responsible for the business and its success is dependant on you, so taking time away from it will have a massive effect on the finances and overall management whilst you are away.

If the time you take away is only short, i.e. a couple of days, it won't make much impact on the business.

One week away will mean that you will have to work a little harder just before and just after that week as you catch up with all the patients who have been squeezed into the clinic before you go away, and then there are those you have to fit in when you return. You finances won't change much as you will probably earn more just before and just after, making up for the week away.

If you decide to take two weeks away, it will start to affect your business. If someone rings up to get an appointment whilst you are away, they may not be able to get an appointment for several weeks because patients have been squeezed in before and after your time away. You will then lose a hard earned patient to someone else. Taking two weeks away can start to affect your finances. You will still have certain expenses to meet, even though you may not physically be in the clinic working. You have stock sitting waiting to be used or sold. Receptionist's wages to meet as they will still be answering the phone while you are away. Utilities and business rates will need to be paid. Insurance payments to keep up to date as well as rent, lease or mortgage repayments to make. You have got to think seriously about the impact of taking two or more weeks away from the business, after all, it relies on you to work to generate the money which covers the expenses.

If you decide to pay someone to cover your absense while you are away, you will have to be able to trust them implicitly. If your patients don't like them or the treatment they provide is of a poor standard, you will start to lose patients and it could become a very expensive time away. Even if they are a suitable substitute for you, you will still have their fees to pay. Is it going to be cost effective?

What about your drawings for the time away? Will you still pay yourself the same amount that you normally do every month, or will you pay yourself an amount proportionate to the time spent working? How will this effect your personal finances if you are not taking as much from the business as you need to survive?

At the beginning of a business, it may be more prudent to take shorter holidays, spread over the year. Why not consider taking long weekends, or booking time off around bank holidays, so that you are only away from the business a couple of days, but effectively on holiday for four or five. You could even combine a few days away with an education course for CPD activity. It may seem a bit unfair, but when you decided to become self employed you also decided to make some small personal sacrifices in order to develop a successful business. As it grows you will have the finances and sustainability to go away when you wish.

C

Growing and Developing Your Practice

29 Expanding your services

Up to now, we have mainly been basing your successful practice on providing only routine Podiatry, but to get a broader range of patients you will need to offer a different variety of services, in response to patients needs and expectations.

Now that you have established the basics you may wish to provide a Biomechanical service, Diabetic Assessments, Nail Surgery, Domiciliaries and Nursing Home treatments or sell additional retail products.

Biomechanics

This area of Podiatry comes with prestige and greater wealth, if done correctly. Before including a Biomechanics service in your practice, it is a good idea to go on several training courses, do background reading and have a greater understanding of the subject. If you don't, you will quickly gain a reputation for having a lack of knowledge, and for charging patients large amounts of money without diagnosing or prescribing properly. You cannot provide the same insoles to everyone, they will need assessing and diagnosing on an individual basis.

A Biomechanics service will be entirely based and maintained on your reputation and the success you produce.

It is very difficult to advertise a Biomechanical service, as patients don't know what it is and won't understand its relevance to them and their problem. Virtually all of your referrals for this service will come from GPs, Consultants, Other Health Professionals, Sports Clubs, Gyms and other successfully treated patients. If you don't know what you are doing, no one is going to refer patients to you.

The worse case scenario is that you don't diagnose properly and thereby cause further problems. If this is a serious, competitive athlete, it could have a huge effect on your business as we slowly become a more litigious nation. You could be responsible for damaging an athletes career.

If you feel you are competent enough to provide a biomechanical service there are a lot of things you will need to consider.

Stationery

Devise a Biomechanical assessment form to suit your requirements. If you have image capturing equipment, you may also wish to include these in your patients records.

An example of a basic assessment form is included in Appendix C. A Biomechanical assessment can be an individual thing, so adapt the form to allow quick access to the information which you feel is relevant to you.

Advertising and Promotion

As has already been mentioned, your reputation in this field will be the main source of new patients. Good continual communication with GPs, Consultants and other health professionals is essential in order to build up strong relationships. Once they know what you are capable of, they will happily refer their patients for your opinion.

If you have image capturing software, it is a great promotional tool (as well as diagnostic). A physical image of your assessment is a wonderful permanently captured view as well as an impressive way to promote yourself to others.

Write to local Sports Clubs, Gyms, Ramblers Clubs and Athletics Groups to introduce your services and offer them a promotional talk. Also, aim high for local Football Clubs and Cricket Clubs and offer an advice service for free, it will give you experience dealing with demanding professional sports people, as well as wonderful promotion.

Using image capturing equipment can be a great educational tool for other professionals. Why not invite local Physiotherapists, Osteopaths, other Podiatrists, Sports Trainers and any other potential sources of referral to attend a days education on Gait Analysis and how your equipment can be used. Now they know you have the equipment and know how to use it, they will refer more patients to you. They are also going to be good quality referrals, now that the other professionals are more educated and understand your relevance to their patients well being.

CE Registration

You will need to register with the Medical Devices Agency if you are manufacturing custom made devices for your patients such as;

* Casted Foot Orthotics made inhouse

* Simple Insoles manufactured inhouse

* Scotch Cast boots

If you are ordering a device with a prescription from an orthotic laboratory, you will not need to register, however the laboratory will.

For most clinical chairside devices you will not need to register, including;

* Padding and strapping

* Silicone devices

* Additions to custom made devices

* Additions to premanufactured devices

* Footwear alterations.

If you are in any doubt, contact the Medical Devices Agency for their advice.

Diabetic Assessments and Monitoring

As already mentioned in the section to do with Biomechanics, if you intend to provide additional services you have got to make sure you are competent and have the appropriate skills to provide it professionally. You may need to go on training courses to update you skills.

Your Podiatry clinic may already be providing routine treatments to some of your patients who are Diabetic. As part of your routine treatment you should already be asking questions about the state of their Diabetes, their blood monitoring results and investigations into their nerve and blood supplies. Taking it one step further to include a more thorough investigation would be the natural progression to develop a Diabetic Service within your practice. But have you enough Diabetic patients to justify the expense of buying specific Diabetic assessment equipment? Is there a market for such assessments? Would you be duplicating a service already provided at GP practices, Hospitals or NHS Clinics?

Instead of trying to expand within your existing practice, some GPs may be more interested in getting you to provide in-house Diabetic Assessments within their practice.

Stationery

You will need a specific Diabetic Assessment form to complete. Make sure it is simple to understand, so you can send it to others and they can interpret it as well as you.

A basic Diabetic form, like the example in Appendix C, can be adapted to suit your own needs. If you are going to be working with other health professionals in your management of Diabetes, it would be a good idea to ask them what they would like included and how to standardize it between professions, so you are all working closer together.

When you have completed a yearly Diabetic review, send a copy to the patients GP for their record, so that they have an ongoing record of their patients Diabetic health.

Advertising

The most effective way of promoting a Diabetic service is to get in touch with local GPs and provide it to their patients through them. Advertising in a newspaper that Diabetic assessments are available at your clinic will not yield much response. Work closely with patients' GPs and Nurses as most of your referrals will come from them.

Keep a list of when a patient should need an assessment. Send them a letter reminding them that they are due, or better still; a postcard with a picture of feet on the front. If they pin it on a board or on the fridge, it's a constant reminder as opposed to a letter getting filed away and forgotten.

Education is also a great way to encourage more awareness of Diabetic monitoring. Offer free talks to your local GP practices and Diabetic groups and you will soon find that they will put into practice what they have learnt from you, and from then on always use you as a source of information and advice.

Nail Surgery

If you are qualified to administer Local Anesthetics and perform Nail Surgery this can be a valuable service to provide for patients with recurrent ingrowing toenails and may often be something unique to your practice as opposed to some of your competitors.

Additional Stationery

When you assess a patient for nail surgery, you will need a consent form which they can then sign to confirm you have gone through the patients medical history, the procedure, risks and costs.

It is useful to include written risks and conditions on this form but make sure the patient has read it before they sign.

A nail surgery procedure form will need to be completed when the patient has the operation, as well as an information sheet or leaflet for the patient to take home. It is a good idea to provide patients with a leaflet about what they themselves need to do after the operation, so that they are in possession of all the information as well as what is expected of them.

They should also be in possession of your mobile phone number in case they need to contact you immediately after the operation. If you provide them with thorough and concise information and answer all their questions before, they probably won't need to contact you anyway.

Examples of these additional stationery requirements are included in Appendix C.

Advertising and Promotion

You could send an Information leaflet accompanying a letter to all the local GP's advising them of the service you now offer.

If you intend to perform nail surgery on a patient, it is professional of you to inform the patients GP of your intention to operate. It also provides valuable promotion. Make your letter informative and knowledgeable. When the wound has healed, send a final report to the GP explaining the outcome. As time goes on, the local doctors will become aware of your ability to provide Nail Surgery and will eventually start to refer patients to you specifically for surgery.

Domiciliary

If you wish to expand your practice by including home visits, you will need to be aware of a few additional considerations.

* You will need transport

* You will need to allow time to get to and from the visit

* Safety Considerations

* Poor working conditions

* Additional waste disposal arrangements

To physically get to the home to visit a patient, you are going to need transport. If this is your own car, or the businesses car, you are going to need to incorporate the cost of using the car, wear and tear, the insurance and petrol into the fee you charge. Traveling to the patient, then away from them when you are done is also going to increase the charge for a home visit. To make any money out of a home visit you would realistically have to charge the patient more than they would be willing to pay, but you have to keep it realistic.

Other considerations you need to be aware of are to do with safety and working conditions. If you are entering someone else's home, your safety could be at risk. It is a good idea to have a mobile phone with you at all times and let someone else know where you've gone or when you expect to be finished. Ladies may find that carrying a 'rape alarm' is also a good idea.

Because you are not providing treatment in a clinical environment, with all your equipment available to make the work more comfortable, you may suffer from back trouble as a result of providing home visits. The patient will be sitting on their chair and you may be sat on a chair with their foot on your knee or on the floor with their foot on a foot stool. If the patients mobility is poor, they are also unlikely to be able to lift their feet very high for you to get a good view of what you are working on. However you decide to operate, it will not be ideal.

Try to adopt a position which provides some lower back support, perhaps by using a cushion behind you. Avoid leaning forward too much and bending your neck to extremes.

Alternative waste disposal arrangements will also need to be considered.

Advertising

Put up a poster in your clinic announcing the home visiting service. Patients often know of an infirm relative or friend who may be interested in having Podiatry done at home.

Send letters introducing yourself to local Nursing homes and offer your services to them. Most homes employ the use of a Podiatrist for their residents. Calculate a discounted rate for them as you will often do bulk treatments using very little supplies, with no additional mileage and no rent. Residents in nursing homes often have very few problems with their feet and it is often quite quick and easy to treat a large volume in one day. 20-30 patients in a Nursing home in one day is quite possible.

If you can, try and alternate days when you are at a Nursing Home with days in the clinic. Too much time spent in an inadequate treating position could cause long term back problems.

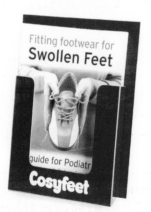

30 Selling Products

A good way of generating more money without having to physically do any more work, is to sell things. Enhance your practice by selling the items you recommend to your patients. Be careful not to push your sales too hard, otherwise it will distance your patients from you and you may lose them as a regular customer at the expense of trying to get them to buy a tube of cream. This could also result in negative feedback about your business and affect your reputation.

Another thing you should be aware of is to only sell the products you personally feel confident in and have seen positive results from. In order to recommend products you will need to know a little about them so that you can explain to the patient why it's in their interest to use it. For example, explain to them what makes this cream better than that cream and why it's relevant to them.

Supplies

Choose what products you are going to sell. A large range will require a large supply of stock and will effect your cash flow, with spare cash being held in products waiting to be purchased. If you keep a large stock of products you will also need to have adequate storage space, which adds to the cost of supplying products to your patients.

Start with a basic range of items which patients may regularly ask about or need.

Small Range	
Creams	Files
Nippers	Shoe Horns

If you have the storage space and the available money to invest, then expand your product range, but try to avoid overlapping many different types of one product to avoid patients confusion as to which product is better.

Large Range	
Anti fungal Creams	Toe Devices
Verrucae Home Treatment	Polymer Gel Products
Paddings and Strappings	Off the shelf insoles/orthotics

Costing

Work out the individual cost of each product, as most products will come in boxes or bulk purchases. Many companies will give you discounts when buying in bulk. Another way to get them at a cheaper price is to buy direct from the manufacturer or distributor. Look on the packaging for the manufacturer or distributor contact details and get in touch. Ask if they sell to individuals and what the minimum order would be.

Once you've worked out the individual cost of getting the product to you (which will include VAT and delivery charges) you will now need to consider your profit margin.

Most products have a 20% mark up on their cost. Don't forget the Income Tax charge, as any profit you make is subject to taxation. In effect you should increase your mark up to 37%

Example

A Tube of cream costs you £2.45 and your mark up is 37%
Calculation is £2.45 X 1.37
Total cost to the patient is therefore £3.36
Total profit per tube of cream is 91p

You won't make a huge amount from reselling products, but it's additional income which doesn't involve you having to do anything. The more you stock and sell, the more you will make, but are you a salesmen or a Podiatrist? The more products that you have available, the more baffling to patients it may be. Particularly if you sell several different creams which all claim to do the same thing.

Advertising and Promotion

Make the most of the space available to you in the clinic or reception area. Have attractive stands or displays where patients can see what is available and posters with pictures of the products being used. Print some labels with your name, address and phone number on and attach them to the products so that patients are reminded of where they got it from, where they can get more from and where they can tell their friends to get it from.

If you are packaging up felt, tape, toe devices etc., why not put them in bags or wrapping with your name and business details on.

Every now and then, do a special offer on certain products. It's a good way to introduce patients into using certain products which hopefully, they will keep buying from you in the future.

At Christmas, box together a few of your most popular products and sell them as seasonal gift boxes for patients to give to their friends or relatives.

Another product you can sell is Gift Vouchers. Patients will always know someone who needs Chiropody and a Gift Voucher is an excellent and unique gift. As well as improving your cashflow, it introduces a new patient to you, who will hopefully become a frequent visitor. It also provides a talking point between the person who bought the voucher and their friends, as well as the person who received the voucher and their friends. This is all free advertising for the clinic.

To promote the clinic relatively cheaply, you could donate a Gift Voucher to local school raffles, or Retirement Centre raffles. It's cheaper than newspaper advertising and generates additional advertising by word of mouth.

31 Moving Premises

There may be several reasons why you may need to relocate after a period of time, some of which may include;

* Requiring additional space

* To reduce your costs

* A more suitable location

* A change in circumstances

* The end of a lease contract

Although overall, a move should be for the positive effect it should have on your business, there are also disadvantages caused by the relocation. Before you make the decision to relocate your business you will have to consider all of the disadvantages caused by the upheaval, especially since your main type of customer, the elderly, may not like or respond well, to change.

Consider how you can make the change to a different location smooth and simple for your patients, because if they don't move with you, you will need to spend money readvertising and building up your patient list again. This could result in being a costly and harmful way to develop your business.

You should also consider the effect relocation may have on your staff. They may find the change stressful, or the location more difficult to get to. For the move and subsequent growth of the business you should try to maintain you staff to the best of your abilities. Discuss with them the reasons for relocation, ask their opinions on the new premises, if the work increases offer them a wage increase because of the new responsibilities and increased workload. Make sure you are available to answer any question or concern, however trivial it may seem, that an employee has. If your employees jobs are not at risk then make sure they understand that. This is likely to be their greatest worry. They may also be concerned over a change in job description. Reassure them if no change is likely, but if it is, then sit down and discuss what their new role will include. You will also need to have a new contract drawn up if their job description changes. There may be a certain amount of retraining to be done if your staff will be expected to use a new computer system for example, at the new premises.

If the new premises are in a totally separate area, you are unlikely to retain both staff and patients and will have to start the process of developing a business all over again.

When you chose the location for the initial premises you under-took research and planning on where the best place would be to have a practice. Reapply this to the new premises to make sure that it is the most suitable for your current needs as well as future ones. You should not make a habit of moving every couple of years as your business grows.

Don't wait for certain circumstances to occur, like the end of the lease, before taking the decision to move, this will result in hasty decision making and mistakes being made. Think ahead and predict a change in location and start planning or considering all possibilities before the need arises.

Planning effectively will ensure changes occur smoothly, without any major hiccups and stays within your budget. You will need to assess what possible risks the change will create for the business and how best it will be to reduce or avoid those risks. What would happen if your new premises were not ready on time? You would have a period where no patients are being treated. What if your refurbishment costs prove to be higher that expected? Could you raise the additional capital?

Now imagine yourself in the new premises and ask yourself key questions;

* Is it suitable for your patients?

* Will it put you in a better position to develop?

* If you currently work with other professionals, will they still refer patients to you?

* Will your new premises give you an advantageous competative edge?

Think objectively about the answers to important questions which are relevant to the business. Don't just tell yourself the answers you want to hear. Why not contact a business advisor and ask for their opinion, they may be able to help you look at things from a more impartial position.

If you currently work in premises with other professionals, what will happen when you leave? Will they replace you and your service? If so, will patients be loyal to you or to the practice as a whole? If it is the practice, you are likely to leave patients behind and have to develop a business again from your new premises.

Set yourself objectives for the move and a timescale of when you would expect to achieve them. This will give you a better understanding of how the move is going and whether it is on target for the proposed opening date.

Another important factor you will need to consider is how you intend to communicate your change of address to past, present and future patients? You could put up a sign in the present clinic announcing the imminent change of premises and when it will be open. Provide them with information, including leaflets, directions and maybe even an incentive voucher, for their next appointment, if it will be at the new address.

It may be a long and laborious task, but send out a postcard to your patients telling them of the change of address. You may decide to only send a card to those patients who have been to the clinic in the last 6 or 12 months, or you may want to send one to every patient you have a record for. However many you decide to send, don't forget to budget for postage and printing costs.

Another way to promote your new premises is to contact the local newspaper and invite them to the clinic when it is complete to write a feature on you and the clinic. Back it up with an advert in the same newspaper issue and entice patients into the clinic with incentives, e.g. 20% off all routine treatments for the first month. However you decide to do it, just make sure you get your name and new address out to your patients. If you don't and they arrive at the old address, they may feel that their custom is not valued by you and may take it elsewhere.

Don't forget your suppliers. Make sure they know the new address so that deliveries go to the correct location. Telephone and inform them of the new address, get them to update their records and back it up with a written letter explaining the new location for your business.

Contact the post office and arrange for mail to be relocated for a certain period of time, so you don't miss any important letters still getting sent to the old address.

Don't change location just for the sake of it. Make sure it is for all the right reasons and is not just because you feel the need for change. Look at your current situation, if it still provides all the things the business needs to operate and grow, stay where you are, it is less costly, less likely to lose you customers and a lot less stressful.

32 Extending your Building

If moving premises is not an option that appeals to you, or would not suit your business, then you could always consider extending your present building. You will only be able to do this if you own the building. If you rent or lease the property you will not be able to make any structural changes without the permission of the owner.

Extending your practice could provide additional income generating space which you could rent out to other professionals, or use as an overflow for your own business. If you do not have to relocate, there will be no readvertising expenses and it reduces the risk of losing patients on the way. If you add to the existing building, you will, of course, need to apply to your local authority for planning permission to extend or externally alter the building. Make sure you have sufficient funding in place to pay for the extension before building work starts. If you have a mortgage on the building, you may be able to extend the amount you have borrowed to pay for the improvements.

Submit plans of the existing building and extension, its size, construction details and proposed use. The authority will charge you for submitting an application. Usually you will have a decision from the authority within five weeks. If they are not satisfied with the plans they may ask you to make alterations.

You will need to make sure your extension complys to building regulations, including amongst many things fire safety, sound proofing, ventilation and drainage. You may also have to show that your premises will allow easy access for disabled people. The builder you use will be responsible for ensuring work complies with the building regulations, but check before proceding. If the regulations are not adhered to an enforcement notice may be issued requiring you to make alterations or even removing the building all together.

As building progresses an approved inspector, usually appointed by the local authority, will check the building work and when complete, issue you with a final certificate. A fee is also payable to the inspector.

33 **Branch Practices**

Instead of moving premises, why not consider setting up another practice in a separate area? This is called a Branch Practice, and although it would be in a different area, it would still belong to the business you already have and as long as you have the staff to run it, you would not have to stop working at your current location. There could be many reasons why you would want to start another practice in conjunction with the one you already have, including;

* You may have reached a limit on the number of patients you can physically treat at your current practice

* You may have reached a limit on the space or time available to you at your current location

* You may have identified a lack of services in a neighbouring area and wish to exploit it

* You may want to provide your services to a larger audience over a larger area

* You want the challenge of starting a business from scratch again

* You may simply want to expand the business to maximise profits

If you decide to open a branch practice, certain aspects of setting up a business will still apply as they did when you started your initial venture. You must still do all the preparation and research into the location you are looking at for the branch practice, if it is not right then even businesses who have shown success, will still not thrive there.

The fact that you have already got a successful business will encourage investors to happily provide any financial input to a new venture, particularly if it is the same as the existing one and in a location which has potential to generate significant profits. However, if the branch practice doesn't run as efficiently or as profitable as the initial practice, you may find it draining the resources and money of the original practice and making the business suffer.

Managing more than one practice at a time may have its share of paperwork, but you have already created a successful business, so if you follow your proven business model for another practice, it should be less stressful than the initial venture was. It may also give you the flexibility to work in different locations every week, thereby adding variety to your work. Alternatively, you may wish to only work in one practice, but organise other Podiatrists to work for you at the branch practice.

Running a Branch practice in conjunction with your existing practice can also save you money, as you can purchase in bigger quantities and gain savings on supplies and retail stock.

You can have any number of Branch Practices, it is totally up to you and depends on your drive to create a bigger business, or whether you are satisfied with what you have already achieved.

34 Taking on another Podiatrist

As your practice grows and develops you may find that you have physically got too much work to do by yourself. This is when you should start to consider employing the services of another Podiatrist. There are several ways you can do this, each with its own benefits, but however you decide to do it, they need to be suitable for the business, because the work they do will reflect on you and your business. If patients take a dislike to the new Podiatrist or don't feel that the treatment they received is of a caliber they have been used to from you, they are unlikely to come back again and other people will get to hear about it, as negative advertising soon spreads.

Up to now, the business has relied on you alone. You have put in the extra effort to make sure the business is a success. How can you ensure another Podiatrist will do the same? However, if you find the right Podiatrist, they can bring additional skills and expertise to enhance your practice and increase the number of patients who visit.

Employing a Podiatrist as an employee.

The obvious way of getting another Podiatrist to work for you is to simply employ one. The implications of employing someone whether it is full or part time, have been discussed in a previous section. Is an employment contract incentive enough for a Podiatrist to put in as much dedication and commitment as yourself? You may want to include incentives such as Pension contributions, a vehicle or mobile phone to encourage hard work and a sense of loyalty and dedication to the business.

The advantages of employing someone are:

* You financially know how much the wage of the Podiatrist will be each month and can budget accordingly

* You will have a Podiatrist who can build up a relationship with patients over time

* There is someone you can rely on to cover holiday leave when necessary

* They may wish to buy the business from you when you decide to retire

* You financially gain from the work they do for you

* You will have another colleague to discuss patients and treatments with

* They can bring additional skills to the business

* It takes some of the responsibility off you as you will not have to treat everyone who comes through the door

* It allows the business to expand

* Although they will be left to treat patients, you still have some input into standards of treatment and your expectations as an employer

Unfortunately there are certain disadvantages;

* As an employer you are responsible for Tax and National Insurance contributions and all the paperwork involved

* You will have to give paid holiday, even though no income is being generated from that Podiatrists workload

* You will need to provide adequate training to meet CPD activity levels

* They may leave and take patients away with them

* Employees are entitled to sick leave, maternity leave and other benefits

* You will have to give up some control over patient treatment to someone else

* You will have to learn to deligate

    If you employ a Podiatist you will have to organise their Tax and National Insurance contributions, as well as provide adequate Insurance. Make sure you draw up an employment contract which is signed and agreed before they start work. It may be wise to incorporate a trial period within the contract so that you can terminate the contract if they don't fit in or if they decide working for you is not suiting them.

    When deciding on what level of pay to provide the Podiatrist, look around at other vacant positions and NHS pay scales to see what you will be competing with. Take into account the costs you will be responsible for in allowing another Podiatrist to treat patients within your practice.

Example

The following example is based on a Podiatrist treating 16 patients in one day priced at £17 per patient. Total takings for the day would be £272. If you paid the Podiatrist £12 per hour, totalling £96 for an 8 hour day, you would be left with £39.20 per day.

Expenditure	Basis of calculation	Cost	Formulae
Possible Materials Used		£ 16 . 00	£1 X 16
Rent	Based on an 8 hour day costing £50 rent	£ 50 . 00	
Use of equipment	Based on life span of 25,000 treatments, costing £4,000	£ 2 . 56	£4,000 / 25,000 X 16
	Sub Total	£ 68 . 56	
Savings for Tax	17.5%	£ 47 . 60	£272 X 0.175
Savings for National Insurance	7%	£ 19 . 04	£272 X 0.07
	Total	£ 135 . 20	
	Profit per day	£ 136.80	£272 – 135.20

Explanation of the table

It is very difficult to calculate what material you will use and how much it will cost. By breaking down packs and boxes into singular units you can estimate what the cost would be for one patient. The rent is based on working an eight hour day costing £50. Wear and tear on equipment is an estimate. 25,000 treatments is approximately a life span of about 6-7 years in a full time practice. You will be taxed on the price you charge the patients, so budget for tax and National Insurance Contributions.

You will be responsible for the cost of providing adequate training, although they should pay their own professional fees. You will also have the expense of paying their annual leave as well as other incentives, such as Pension or Vehicle expenses. This gradually reduces the profit you make from the work they do.

Using a Freelance Podiatrist

Another way of having a Podiatrist work for you is to employ a freelancer or contractor. This type of employment is sometimes called 'fee sharing.' These are self employed Podiatrists who are responsible for their own tax affairs and only get paid for the work they do. Therefore, they are responsible for their own holiday pay and all other benefits normally provided by an employer. You still have a responsibility to provide a safe working environment for others who work for you, even though they are classed as self employed.

Advantages of using a self employed Podiatrist;

* You are not responsible for their tax returns and are not required to organise their tax and National Insurance Contributions

* You do not have to provide Holiday Pay, Sick Pay, Maternity Pay or any other benefit you would normally provide for an employee of the business

* They may feel a duty to provide a high standard of care, otherwise they may not be asked back to do more work as

they do not have an employment contract

* They are responsible for their own training, CPD activities and professional fees

* Provide flexible work for certain lengths of time, or as required

* They can provide additional or alternative skills to the business

    Disadvantages include;

* They will require a higher pay or percentage of the work they provide for you

* They may lack the commitment to the job or business if they know that the work is only available for a certain length of time

* May leave and take patients away with them and become direct competition to your practice

* May have a carefree attitude to patient care, as they know they might not see the patient again

When deciding how much to pay a freelance Podiatist, don't forget that there are no additional expenses or incentives to pay them as you would with an employee of the business. Because you will have no responsibilities to them like a normal employee, a freelance Podiatrist will expect a much higher income from the work they have done. This is often a percentage of the fees they generate or a set fee for a day or mornings work, or an hourly rate. A freelance Podiatrist will often specify or ask for a certain payment before working for you. Do your calculations and see if their payment is viable once you have taken into account all your expenses, if not, you need to look elsewhere or negotiate with the Podiatrist to work for a fee which suits you. Do not use a freelance Podiatrist if their fee and your expenses are going to be more than the income generated by the patients treated.

Associates

You may also like to consider running a business with an Associate. This is when two or more Podiatrists are working on the same premesis or in a separate practice. This may be a suitable way of getting long term commitment to the business from another Podiatrist. Finding an associate for your business can be a lengthy process, as you need to consider their personal goals and professionalism, before tailoring the financial aspect of their input to the business. You will need to spend time and effort in building up a relationship with the Associate who must be like minded and share the same vision for the business as you do.

Taking on an Associate is a long term relationship. They are also classed as self employed and pay their own Tax and National Insurance contributions

Advantages include;

* Higher level of dedication as they are equally responsible for the success of the business

* You will be introducing long term additional skills to the business

* Someone else who can provide support to you

* They may wish to buy the business from you when you decide to retire

* You will have a Podiatrist who can build up a relationship with patients over time

* Someone to keep the business running when you are on holiday

* It allows the business to expand

  Disadvantages of an associate;

* They could be a financial burden if they don't fit the business

* There may be personality clashes

* May leave and take patients away with them and become direct competition to your practice

You will need to look at your overheads and expenses to calculate what percentage of the profit an Associate will take. It will need to be based on the value of the income they generate or patients they bring to the business. The percentage an Associate may take could be 45%-60% of their gross earnings. You may prefer to offer a stepped salary, ie meeting certain targets increases the level of profit they take. They will also need to be self employed and pay Tax and National Insurance on the profit they take.

If in doubt about what format would suit your business, talk to your Accountant or business advisor, who may be able to provide you with more specific information and advice about your business. As with all employees, contractors or associates, check the applicants references thoroughly and always provide a written contract or job description to the Podiatrist, before allowing them to start work.

35 Using Locums

To fill short term vacancies, such as those created by holidays, you may find it useful employing the services of a locum. Contact Locum agencies advertised in your professional journal and they should be able to provide you with a list of suitable candidates for your job. You will pay a fee to the agency who in turn pay the Locum, although the Locum will be under your control when working for you.

The advantages of employing a Locum include;

* You will have no advertising costs to find a suitable candidate

* There will be no need for interviewing

* You will not have the responsibility of organising the Locum's pay, Tax or National Insurance contributions

* You do not need to arrange sick pay, maternity pay or paid annual leave

* Temporarily fills gaps in your workload

* Contracts can be terminated relatively quickly if the Locum does not fit into the business

* They are responsible for their own training and membership to the correct governing bodies

However, there are certain negative aspects of employing a Locum you should consider;

* You have a responsibility for the Locums health and safety

whilst they work for you

* They will not have the same dedication to the business that an employee may have

* They may terminate the contract relatively quickly if the work does not suit them

* Other employees may be unhappy at the pay difference between themselves and Locum staff

* They may move on at short notice if they find another job they like better

Employing Locums can be a quick, easy and efficient way of filling gaps in your workforce, whether it's a Podiatrist or Receptionist you are looking for. A Locum is a short term solution to a problem. If you have a vacancy which may be long term, try to get it filled as soon as possible. There are many more advantages to a steady, regularly employed work force than continuing to use Locums.

36 Renting Space to other Professionals

If you own the property you are working from and you have a vacant room, why not rent it out to someone else? If you are leasing the property, you can sub let a room to someone else in exactly the same way as if you owned it.

By making full use of the entire practice, you will reduce the expenses of running the practice, as well as advertising your services to customers who visit the person who is renting from you. Make sure that the room is suitable to use and meets minimum standards, then decide what sort of professional you would like to rent the room to. The presence of another health professional gives the practice a good image and works well in conjunction with the services you already provide. A Physiotherapist, Osteopath, Chiropractor or Reflexologist are obvious choices. Patients of these would also be likely to visit you as well. Although you can have anyone in your spare room you must consider the image it would portray to other health professionals, such as GPs, if you work in a practice with a hairdresser. It may look like you are providing a beauty therapy as opposed to a medical service.

Once you have decided what sort of professional you would like to work with, you must make contact with them. This can be done through their professional journals, advertising you room to rent, or look in the Yellow Pages and write to all the local professionals inviting them to the practice to look at the room available.

You will also need to consider how much you are going to charge them for the use of the room. Think about the amount of practice expenses you have, including mortgage repayments, reception staff, business rates, utilities and insurance, then think of the size of the building and try and work out the cost per square meter. Apply this to the size of the room you are renting out to give you an idea of a fair rent. Some professionals will want to pay a set rate per day or half day, where as others may prefer to pay a percentage of the fees they take, to you.

189

Fee sharing can suit the other professional at the start whilst they build up a list of patients, as they are only paying when they are earning. Later on, once they are established, they may prefer a set fee for the time they are in the practice.

As with employees of your business, you are responsible for the health and safety of another professional if they are working on your premises. They are responsible for their own Tax and National Insurance contributions and any other expenses to do with their work or professional body.

Be careful who you choose to rent a room to. If they develop a bad reputation, then so will you. Although you are not responsible for the work they do, your practice will become synonymous with poor work.

37 Selling Your Practice

There are a number of things you need to consider before being able to sell your practice. Will the sale of your business be a means of investing for your retirement or will you keep some form of management or supportive role?

There are different types of sale options:

* Full or Partial sale. Sell the entire business or retain partial ownership to assist the new owner in managing the business.

* Sale of assets. Sell off anything the business owns, including equipment, property, supplies and patient lists.

* Full or installment payments. Payment for the business can be made when the business is sold or in installments.

To assist with the sale you will need the services of an Accountant and Solicitor. The Accountant will need to prepare the accounts, where as the Solicitor handles the legal issues.

Before you sell your business, you will need to prepare it. Make sure the business is in a strong position with a good financial record. Choose when the best time would be to sell and work towards it. Aim to sell when your business is making increasing profits or growing. Showing that your diary is full demonstrates a profitable and sustainable business. In preparation for the sale, you should make sure all equipment is maintained and certified, autoclaves have been serviced and the building is in good repair.

You will need to value the business. This is based on;

* Past, present and future cashflow

* Your position in the market

* The assets

* Goodwill

* Your current employees

* Level of debt

The actual value you place on your business is usually based on multiples of future earnings, taking into account a valuation of the assets

Once you have calculated a value for the business, you will need to target your potential buyers. Who would be interested in buying your business? Other Podiatrists working in the same area may wish to purchase the business. Or someone wishing to relocate.

As you will be targeting other Podiatrists, the best place for advertising will be in the classified section of your professional journal. Potential buyers may prefer you to stay on for a period of 3 - 6 months to guide them through the running of the business, break them into the work and introduce them to the patients.

Meet with potential buyers allowing them to discuss aspects of the business, look around the practice, and ask questions. It also gives you the opportunity to ask them what their proposals are for your employees and whether or not they will require your input once the sale has gone through. They may also want to negotiate on the price.

Before a buyer will put in an offer, they will want to look at your audited accounts. Your will need to discuss with them the structure of the deal and a possible timescale for completion. You should ask for proof that the buyer has the financial means to purchase the business, including mortgage or loan agreements.

You will need to provide legal confirmation that the information you have provided is accurate.

Remember, you may have to pay Capital Gains Tax on the sale of the business. Your Accountant should be able to advise on minimizing your liabilities.

Once the sale has been agreed you will need to agree with the buyer the 'Heads of Terms.' This is a legal document detailing what is being bought and how payment is to be structured. You will also need to list the assets and employee contracts. A Lawyer or Accountant will help you draw up the Heads of Terms.

When the Heads of Terms has been agreed the buyer reviews all aspects of your business, know as 'Due Diligence,' which usually lasts around four weeks.

As due diligence comes to an end, the sale is finalized.

Once you have sold the practice you will need to decide what you will do with the money you have acquired. Advice from a Financial Advisor is essential if you wish to manage your money into old age.

38 Closing a Practice

If you have decided not to or are unable to sell your business, but still want to retire, then you will need to close the practice. This is a lengthy procedure as it involves selling off your assets and paying any outstanding Tax and National Insurance contributions. You also have responsibilities to your staff to make sure they are paid up to date and issued with the relevant legal forms. Of course, your patients will also need to know that you are closing, so you will need to make adequate arrangements to inform them. Suppliers will also need to know that you will be ceasing to trade, as will your local authority who you pay business rates to.

Check on any rental or lease agreements, as they may require lengthy notice before you can close the business down. Some agreements, such as those on loan vehicles or equipment on a rental agreement, may need to be seen through to the end of the agreement or if you are aloud to terminate the agreement, it may involve some financial penalty.

Outside assistance may also be required, so ask the advice of your Solicitor and Accountant. If one of your assets is property, you will also need to get the services of an Estate Agent, to sell the property for you.

If you have employees in the business, you will need to finalise their pay and deductions up to the point of closure. HM Revenue and Customs will need to be informed that you will no longer be employing any staff. They can help guide you on closing your business and its tax implications. Your employees may be entitled to certain National Insurance related benefits as a result of your business closing. Once they no longer work for you, you should issue them with a P45.

Once you have physically closed the business and it is not treating patients and trading, you will have to make sure that any money you are owed is collected and any debts are paid up to the point when the business closed. You will need to inform HM Revenue and Customs that you have closed the business. Include any expenses incurred in the process of closing the business, from your Accountants fees to postage expenses and prepare the final accounts of the business. This will then be assessed by HM Revenue and Customs to calculate your final tax liability.

In the process of selling off the assets of the business, you may also have to pay Capital Gains Tax.

39 Capital Gains Tax

In the process of selling or closing your business you will financially gain from the sale of the assets of the business, which is subject to Capital Gains Tax. This may effect you if you intended to use the proceeds of selling your business as a means of funding your retirement.

A Capital Gain occurs when you sell an asset you own and its value has increased since you acquired it. Capital Gains Tax is the tax levied on this increase in value. Even if you give something away as opposed to selling it, you might still have to pay Capital Gains Tax based on the market value of the asset.

Capital Gains Tax is not paid on transfers of assets between husband and wife or civil partners, provided you are legally married or in a registered partnership and living together. You can reduce the level of tax paid by calculating the length of time the asset has been held. If you have had the asset for one year, the chargeable gain is reduced by 50%, after two or more years the reduction is 25%. Captial Gains Tax is not paid if you sell your home, however, you may be liable to pay some tax if your practice has been based at home.

You will only have to pay Capital Gains Tax if the amount of Capital Gain is equal to or less than £8,500. Private cars, personal effects and goods worth £6,000 or less are exempt from Capital Gains Tax, as are gifts of assets to a chairty, museum or similar institutions.

Once you have calculated your Tax liability, you will need to complete the relevant part of the self assessment tax return pages and send them to HM Revenue and Customs. After the allowance of £8,500 is deducted from your liability you will have to pay 10% on balances between £1 - £2,150, 20% on balances between £2,151 - £33,300 and 40% on balances over £33,300.

Because it can be quite a complex procedure and varies between each individual business, it is highly recommended that you obtain professional advice from your Accountant when calculating your Capital Gains Tax.

197

40 Keep Working At It

Congratulations. If you've got this far you are obviously quite serious about setting up a private Podiatry practice. Even if you have started your practice you should review it annually, produce new cash flow forecasts and assess your environment and its potential for expansion. There might seem like a lot of other things you need to know which may not be Podiatry based, but it only increases the enjoyment you can only get from being your own boss.

Working hard will allow you the opportunities to enjoy your career as well as your life.

Good luck with your venture; you will only get out of it what you put into it.

APPENDIX A

Skeleton Business Plan

1. Business Details

Legal Status of Business?

Name of the Business	
Address of the Business	
Post code	
Telephone Number	
Web Site Address	
E-mail Address	

Brief explanation of Business activities?

Date Business Commenced?

2. Objectives and Aims

What are your short term objectives?

What are your medium term objectives?

What are your long term objectives?

What are your overall future aims and when do you think you can achieve them?

3. Staff (including yourself)

Name	
Position within Business	
Home Address	
Telephone Number	
Date of Birth	

Professional Qualifications and skills?

Relevant experience or training?

Employment history				
Employer	Position	Salary	Dates	
			From	To

Other key personnel:

Name	
Position within Business	
Proposed Salary	
Home Address	
Telephone Number	
Date of Birth	

Qualifications and skills?

4. Premises

Describe your business premises and the advantages of its location in relation to potential patients?

Renting	
Monthly Rent	
What is included in your rent	
Name of Landlord	
Length of rental agreement	

Leasehold	
Annual Lease	
Name of Owner	
Length of Leasehold	

Freehold	
Monthly repayment	
Mortgage outstanding	
Valuation of property	
Name of Mortgage lender	
Length of Mortgage	

Business Rates	
Annual Amount	
Renewal date	

Insurance	
Value of cover	
Brief description of cover	
Annual Premium	
When renewed	

Are the premises adequate for your future requirements?

5. Equipment

List of Equipment required			
Item	Cost	Possible replacement date	Guarantees

6. Services Available

What are the main services provided by your business and what proportion of turnover would you estimate each to contribute?

Service	% Contribution

What market are you aiming for?

What services will be developed in the future and will they require further training or equipment?

What benefit to the business will additional services create?

What amount of stock will you require to provide these services?

What credit terms are available from your suppliers?

7. Customers

Who are your potential customers?

What information have you acquired about the location of your clinic which demonstrates the potential need for your business?

8. Competitors

Who are your main competitors?

What do they charge for similar services?

What are the strengths and weaknesses of your competitors?

How are you going to provide a competitive service compared to your competitors?

9. Promotion

How do you intend to promote your business and sell your services?

Method	Cost

What level of sales are you aiming for in the next 6 months?

What level of sales are you aiming for over the next 12 months?

10. Funding

What is your total borrowing requirement?

How much of this is to purchase equipment?

What level of finance do you intend to invest?

What will be the sources of your funding?

Source	Amount	Interest	Repayment terms

11. Personal Survival Budget

Estimated Expenditure	
Mortgage and/or rent	
Council Tax	
Utilities	
Home Insurance	
Life Insurance	
Investments or savings plans	
Telephone	
Car Tax	
Car Insurance	
Petrol and Maintenance	
HP repayments	
Subscriptions	
Living expenses	
Others (Please state)	
Total Expenditure	

Income	
From other family members	
Part time employment	
Other sources	
Total Income	

Survival Income Requirement	

12. Pricing

What prices are you going to charge for your services and how do they compare with your competitors?

Service	Your Price	Your Competitors Price

What did you base your calculations for pricing on?

13. Financial projections

What is your Annual Gross Profit?

Projected annual sales	
Less direct costs	
Total Gross Profit	

Calculate your Gross Profit Margin:

(Gross profit / projected sales) X 100 = %

Calculate your annual projected overheads:

Expenses	Costs
Indirect costs	
Drawings	
Salaries	
Rent	
Business Rates	
Insurance	
Utilities	
Telephone	
Maintenance	
Advertising	
Professional Indemnity Insurance	
Loan repayments incl. interest	
Other expenses (specify)	
Total overheads	

Calculate the annual turnover required to break even:

$$(\text{Overheads} / \text{Gross Profit Margin}) \times 100 = £$$

Calculate the monthly turnover required to break even:

$$\text{Annual Break Even Turnover} / 12 = £$$

Calculate your estimated profit:

Projected annual sales	
Less annual break even sales	
X Gross profit Margin	
Profit	

14. Personal Asset Statement

Assets	
Value of Home	
Value of other property	
Surrender value of insurance policies	
Cash or savings	
Shares	
Value of Vehicle	
Valuable Collections	
Other (Please specify)	
Total Assets	

Liabilities	
Outstanding mortgage	
HP repayments	
Loans	
Other (Please specify)	
Total Liabilities	

Personal Net Assets	

15. Cash flow Forecast

Cash flow forecast for period			to			
	Month 1		Month 2		Month 3 etc.	
A. Receipts	Budget	Actual	Budget	Actual	Budget	Actual
Sales						
Loans or Grants						
Capital Injected						
Other income						
Total Receipts						

B. Payments						
Purchases - cash						
Purchases - creditors						
Drawings						
Salaries						
Rent						
Utilities						
Telephone						
Insurance						
Professional Fees						
Maintenance						
Bank charges						
HP Repayments						
Loan repayments						
Savings (for tax payments)						
Other (please specify)						
Total Payments						

Net Cash flow (A - B)						
Opening Bank Balance						
Closing Bank Balance						

APPENDIX B

Useful Contacts

Clothing and Uniform
Cloister Uniforms
www.cloister-uniforms.com

Grahame Gardner Ltd,
www.grahame-gardner.com

Simon Jersey Limited,
www.simonjersey.com

Data Protection Register
Information Commissioners
Office,
Wycliffe House,
Water Lane,
Wilmslow,
Cheshire
SK9 5AF
(01625) 545740
Helpline (01625) 545745

Information Commissioners
Office - Scotland
28 Thistle Street,
Edinburgh
EH2 1EN
(0131) 2256341

Information Commissioners
Office - Wales
2 Alexandra Gate,
Ffordd Pengam,
Cardiff
CF24 2SA
(02920) 894929

Information Commissioners
Office - Northern Ireland
Room 101,
Regus House,
33 Clarendon Dock,
Laganside,
Belfast
BT1 3BG
(028) 9051 1270

Equipment and supplies
Bailey Instruments
527 Wilbraham Road,
Chorlton-cum-Hardy,
Manchester.
M21 0UF
0161 8605849
www.baileyinstruments.co.uk

Batten-Edwards Ltd,
17-19 Swanwick Lane
Broughton Leys
Milton Keynes
MK10 9LD
01908 235335
www.batten-edwards.co.uk

Canonbury Healthcare,
2 St James Road,
Brackley,
Northants.
NN3 7XY
01280 706661
www.canonbury.com

D L Townend Son & Sandy
Riverside Court,
Stoney Battery Road,
Longroyd Bridge,
Huddersfield,
West Yorkshire.
HD1 4TW
0845 2304411
www.dltchiropody.co.uk

Hilary Supplies Ltd,
34A Halstead Road
Mountsorrel
Loughborough
Leics
LE12 7HF
0116 2301900
www.hilarysupplies.co.uk
email:
soniak@hilarysupplies.co.uk

Plinth2000
Wetheringsett Manor

Wetheringsett
Stowmarket
Suffolk
IP14 5PP
01449 767887
www.plinth2000.com

Swann-Morton Ltd,
Owlerton Green
Sheffield
S6 2BJ
0114 2344231
www.swann-morton .com

Footwear Suppliers

Cosyfeet
The Tanyard
Leigh Road
Street
Somerset
BA16 0HR
01458 447275
www.cosyfeet.co.uk

Funding and Advice

Business Eye (Wales)
www.businesseye.org.uk

Business Gateway (Glasgow)
www.bgateway.com

Business Link
0845 6009006
www.businesslink.org

Department of Work and Pensions
www.dwp.gov.uk

Department of Trade and
Industry
www.dti.gov.uk

Federation of Small businesses
(FSB)
www.fsb.org.uk

Highlands and Island Enterprise
(Scotland)
www.hie.co.uk

Invest Northern Island (N.I.)
www.investni.com

National Federation of Enterprise
Agencies (NFEA)
www.nfea.com

Natwest Startup Awards
www.startupsawards.co.uk

Princes Trust
www.princes-trust.org.uk

Shell LiveWIRE
www.shell-livewire.org

Gait Analysis Equipment
Everflex UK Ltd
25 Lyveden Road
Northampton
NN4 7ED
01604 742402
www.ever-flex.com

Health and Safety
Department of Health
www.dh.gov.uk

HM Revenue and Customs
Inland Revenue,
Somerset House,
The Strand,
London.
WC2R 1LB
0845 9154515
www.hmrc.gov.uk

Insurers
Association of British Insurers
51 Gresham Street
London
EC2V 7HQ
020 76003333
www.abi.org.uk

Medical Devices Agency
Medical Devices Agency,
Hannibal House,
Elephant and Castle,
London SE1 6TQ
020 79728000
www.medical-devices.gov.uk

Mortgage Broker
National Association of
Commercial Financial Brokers
(NACFB)
01392 491551
www.nacfb.org/choose_broker.asp

Neighbourhood statistics
http://neighbourhood.statistics.go
v.uk/dissemination/

Orthotics Manufacturers
Everflex UK Ltd
25 Lyveden Road
Northampton
NN4 7ED
01604 742402
www.ever-flex.com

Langer Biomechanics
Brookhouse Way,
Cheadle,
Stoke on Trent.
ST10 1SR
01538 755861
www.lbguk.com

Salts Healthcare Ltd
Lord Street
Birmingham
B7 4DS
0121 3332099
www.stepaheadorthosis.co.uk

Orthotics Material Suppliers
A Algeo Ltd,
Sheridan House,
Bridge Industrial Estate,
Speke Hall Road,
Liverpool.
L24 9HB
0151 4481228
www.algeos.com

Waste Disposal Companies

Biffa 0800 307307

Cannon Hygiene Ltd 0800
3283695

Clinicserve Ltd 01243 782288

APPENDIX C

Stationery Samples

Patient Assessment Sheet

Mr. / Mrs. / Ms		Address	
First Name			
Surname			
Date of Birth		Post Code	
GP		Telephone	
Referral Source			

Medical History
Medication
Allergies
Operations
Main Complaint
Other

Patient Treatment Sheet

Date	Treatment	Signature

Patient Referral Sheet

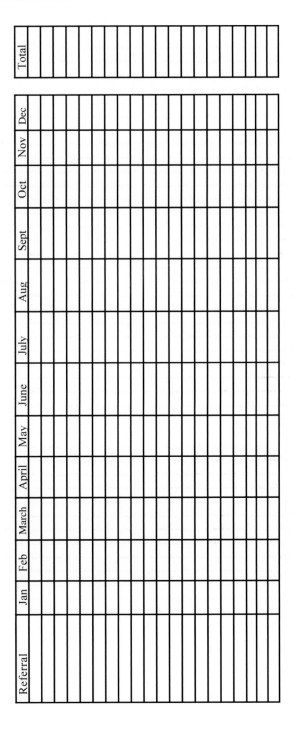

Accounting Sheet

| Month | | | |

Dat	Patient	Amount	Form

| Year | | | |

Date	Patient	Amount	Form

Mileage Form

Month		Year	

Date	From	To	Total Mileage

Business Cards and Appointment cards

Bob Supermax
B.Sc. (Hons) Pod MChS SRCh

Podiatrist

12 Corn Lane,
Nailstone,
Scalpelshire,
SC1 1NS
(01234) 567890

Bob Supermax   (01234) 567890

Date	Time

Please give 24 hours notice if unable to attend, otherwise broken
appointments will be charged for

Biomechanical Assessment Form

Name	
Address	
GP	
Main Complaint	

Measurements	Left	Right
Hip		
Knee		
Ankle		
STJ		
STJ Axis		
MTJ		
1st Ray		
Other Comments		
Management Plan		

Diabetic Monitoring Form

Name	
Address	
GP	
Medical History	
Type of Diabetes	
Medication	
Blood Sugar Levels	
Diet	
Life Style	

Assessment	Left	Right
Pulses		
Nerve Sensation		
Other Comments		
Risk Status		

Nail Surgery Medical History Form

Name	
Address	
Post Code	
Telephone Number	
Date of Birth	
GP	
Are you Diabetic?	
Have you or do you currently have:	
Heart Conditions	
High Blood Pressure	
Anaemia	
Jaundice	
Hepititus	
Asthma	
Rheumatic Fever	
Do you have any blood borne infections	
Have you had a local anaesthetic	
Have you ever had a bad reaction to an	
Are you pregnant	
What medication do you take	
What allergies do you have	
What operations have you had	
Nail Procedure to be performed	
Signed by the patient (or on behalf of a child in your care)	
Date	
Cost	

Nail Surgery Procedure Form

Name	
Address	
Date or Procedure	

Anaesthetic

Patients Weight (Kg)	
Maximum Safe Dose	
Anaesthetic Used	
Batch Number	
Expiry Date	
Volume injected	

Signature of Anaesthetist	

Procedure

Partial Nail Avulsion					
Tib Sulci					
Fib Sulci					
Total Nail Avulsion					
Involuted					
Ingrowing					
Infected					
Tourniquet Time					
Phenol Time					
Dressings applied					
Other information					

Signature of Operator	

Nail Surgery Consent Form

Nail Surgery Consent Form

⚐ The procedure has been explained to you and the medical history form has been completed with your assistance and you now give your permission for the Chiropodist to perform the procedure/s at a mutually convenient date and time. The answers that are on that form were correct at the time of completion and the Chiropodist cannot be held responsible for incorrect, misleading or omitted information.

⚐ The Procedure which is going to be performed is

....

⚐ You must be aware that there is a remote chance that the nail or part of the nail could grow back again at a later date through no fault of the Chiropodist.

⚐ Although precautions are taken to perform the operation in a sterile environment, there is always the risk of infection occurring following the procedure.

⚐ You have a responsibility to help in the healing of the wound and care should be taken to keep the wound clean and dress it as explained by the Chiropodist.

Signed ....
(By the patient or on behalf of a child in your care.)

Name ....

Date ....

APPENDIX D

Written Statement of Employment

Name of employer: Bob Supermax Chiropody and Podiatry
Employer's address: Chiropody Clinic, 12 Corn Lane, Nailstone, Scalpelshire.
Telephone number: 01234 567890

Name of employee: Ivy Tittlebottom
Job title: Receptionist

1. Commencement of employment and continuous employment

Your employment with Bob Supermax Chiropody and Podiatry began on 01/04/2007.

2. Job description

You will be expected to welcome patients to the practice, manage the appointment system and answer phone enquiries. You will also need to take money from patients who have had treatment as well as sell products which may be on display in the waiting area. There will also be patient records to file and retrieve as required.

3. Job location(s)

Your place of work is:
Chiropody Clinic, 12 Corn Lane, Nailstone, Scalpelshire.

4. Pay

Your rate of pay is £6.00 gross per hour.
This will be paid monthly in arrears.

5. Hours of work

You are employed to work Full Time.

Your normal working hours will be 35 hours per week, Monday to Friday, 09:00 and 17:00.
You may occasionally be required to work nights or Saturday mornings.

6.   Holidays
You are entitled to 4 weeks holiday per year, which excludes public holidays.
You will never be required to work public holidays.
Your holiday year begins on 01 April.
You are entitled to carry forward a maximum of 5 days unused holiday to the next holiday year.

7.   Sickness absence
If you cannot work because of illness, you must inform Bob Supermax as early as possible on the first day and each subsequent day when you are unable to work.
Self-certification is not allowed and you must provide a Doctor's Certificate for all periods of absence due to sickness.
You are not entitled to contractual sick pay. You may be entitled to statutory sick pay.

8.   Pension scheme
There is currently no company pension scheme.

9.   Collective agreements with trade unions
There are no collective agreements with trade unions or other employee groups affecting this employment.

10. Ending the employment
This employment is permanent subject to each party's right to terminate in accordance with the terms of this statement.
If you want to leave this employment you must give us minimum statutory notice, i.e. if you have worked for us for at least one month, you must give us at least one week's notice.
We must give you minimum statutory notice if we want to end this employment.
The statutory notice period is:
* one week if your period of continuous employment is longer than

one month but shorter than two years
- one week for each year of continuous employment up to a maximum of 12 weeks

11. Disciplinary procedure

Matters which may be dealt with under this disciplinary and dismissal procedure include discipline and dismissal for the following reasons:

- misconduct
- sub-standard performance
- harassment or victimisation
- misuse of company facilities including computer facilities (eg e-mail and the Internet)
- poor timekeeping
- unauthorised absences

Oral Warning

In the case of minor infringements you may be given a formal oral warning. A note of the oral warning will be kept on your file but will be disregarded for disciplinary purposes after a specified period (e.g. six months). You have the right to appeal against a formal oral warning.

Written Warning

If the infringement is more serious or there is no improvement in conduct after a formal oral warning you will be given a formal written warning giving details of the complaint, the improvement or change in behaviour required, the timescale allowed for this, the right of appeal and the fact that a final written warning may be given if there is no sustained satisfactory improvement or change. A copy of the written warning will be kept on file but will be disregarded for disciplinary purposes after a specified period (eg 12 months).

Final written warning

Where there is a failure to improve or change behaviour during the currency of a prior formal written warning, or where the infringement is sufficiently serious, you may be given a final written warning. This will give details of the complaint, warn that failure to improve will lead to dismissal and refer to the right of appeal. The final written warning will be kept on file but will normally be disregarded for disciplinary purposes after a specified period (eg 12 months).

Dismissal
If your conduct or performance still fails to improve the final step will be to contemplate dismissal as outlined in the Standard Disciplinary and Dismissal Procedure

Gross misconduct
If after investigation it is confirmed that you have committed one of the following offences (the list is not exhaustive), you will normally be dismissed:

- theft
- fraud and deliberate falsification of records
- physical violence
- serious bullying or harassment
- deliberate damage to property
- serious insubordination
- misuse of an organisation's property or name
- bringing the employer into serious disrepute
- serious incapability whilst on duty brought on by alcohol or illegal drugs
- serious negligence which causes or might cause unacceptable loss, damage or injury
- serious infringement of health and safety rules
- serious breach of confidence (subject to the Public Interest (Disclosure) Act 1998).

While the alleged gross misconduct is being investigated, you may be suspended, during which time you will be paid. Any decision to dismiss will be taken by your employer only after a full investigation.

12. I acknowledge receipt of my particulars of employment

Signed .... Dated ....

APPENDIX E

Glossary of Terms

Arrears – A payment still outstanding

Asset – A valuable item

Bad Debt – Occurs when payment is not received or a cheque is returned to you unpaid

Branch Practice – Additional practice run in conjunction with the original practice under the same business

Breakeven – A point where you have neither made a profit nor a loss

Capital – An amount of money invested into a business

Capital Gains Tax (CGT) – Tax levied on profits made on financial gains on a businesses assets, usually when selling or closing a business

Cashflow – The movement of money in and out of the business

Creditors – People who you owe money to

Debt – Money that is owed

Drawings – Money you take from the business as your earnings

Due Diligence – A period of inspection for potential buyers to review all aspects of the business they intend to buy

Employee – Someone who works for a business

Employer – Someone who employs people to help run the business

Expenses – The cost incurred when purchasing something

Freehold – Relating to property. The person will probably have a mortgage on the property and when paid will own the property and the land it is on

Funding – An accumulation of money

Goodwill – Items of a business which are not tangible such as, the reputation of a business and the patients which visit the practice

Gross – Money before any deductions have been taken into account

Heads of Terms – Legal document for potential buyers of a business outlining the details of the sale

Income – Money generated into the business

Leasehold – The owner of the land leases the property to you for a specified time

Maternity – Time before and after a mother is expecting a child

Net – Money after any deductions have been taken into account

Paternity – Time before and after a father is expecting a child

Pay As You Earn (PAYE) – Relates to employees tax and national insurance contributions

Payments – The act of paying

Payroll – A list of employees receiving regular pay

Profit – Financial gain

Profit Margin – Profit after expenses and costs have been taken into account

Pro Rata - Proportionally

Receipts – Amount of money received

Stock Control – Maintaining a level of stock

Transaction – The act of business being done, usually involving money

Turnover – Amount of money taken in the business

Value Added Tax (VAT) – Taxes paid to HM Revenue and Customs